ATOMIC ENERGY

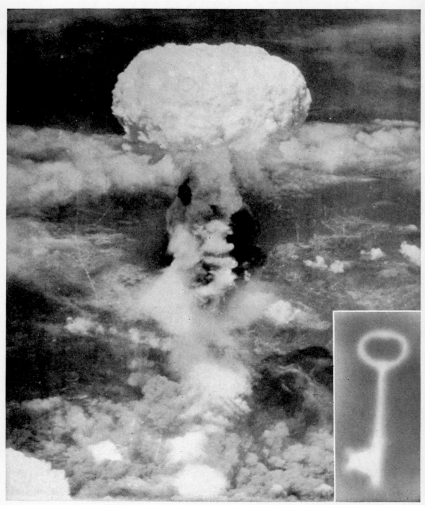

Press Association, Inc.

PLATE I.

The progress of radioactivity through fifty years. An early impression of a key produced by radiation coming from a piece of Uranium-mineral, and the large-scale liberation of the same energy over the Japanese city of Hiroshima.

ATOMIC ENERGY
IN COSMIC AND
HUMAN LIFE

FIFTY YEARS OF RADIOACTIVITY

BY GEORGE GAMOW

CAMBRIDGE: AT THE UNIVERSITY PRESS
NEW YORK: THE MACMILLAN COMPANY

1946

PRINTED IN THE UNITED STATES OF AMERICA
BY J. J. LITTLE & IVES COMPANY, NEW YORK

DEDICATED
TO THE HOPE
OF LASTING PEACE

FOREWORD

Through Professor Gamow's courtesy, I have had the privilege of reading his book in manuscript. I commend it heartily to the general reader—and also to the physicist, who will derive much pleasure from the way that things are put.

May I particularly commend the manner in which the author has brought out the practical and ethical complications which attend the use of atomic energy for the purposes of peace—however valuable in themselves? It is earnestly to be hoped that the thorough protective measures against the dangerous and treacherous radiation, which were so successful in protecting personnel in the war-time developments, will be rigidly required in all industrial applications in the future. The very ingenious suggestion of "atomic storage-batteries" presents a hopeful possibility here, but one that seems likely to be practical only when "high power is needed regardless of cost."

There is an ethical factor in the situation which has been almost completely ignored in most of the voluminous discussion of this subject. The energy stored in atomic nuclei has been locked up in there since the universe came into existence in its present form, and its liberation from each particular atom is the most hopelessly irreversible process that we know of. It is initially set free at a vastly higher potential than any other known form of energy—that is, it is capable of supplying power for a great variety of reactions which no other known process can activate at all. The speculative suggestion of space-traversing ships is realizable in no other way. After a century of investigation, the number of other unique applications of nuclear energy may be expected to be large, and the value of some of them very great.

Yet popular discussion has centered around cheapening the things we already have—transportation, light and power, and even domestic heating. These are processes which can be powered by all the common forms of low-potential energy supply.

Even in these days of frantic reconversion, we may well stop and think of our moral responsibility, as members of the human race, to the longer future. We may use up these irreplaceable supplies of energy—or at least the best part of them —during the coming century in lowering our monthly bills, or in joy-riding, if we find out how to do it safely. What will future generations think of us when they realize what great things might have been done with the supplies which we casually wasted to get our comforts or amusements a little cheaper?

The immediate perils of the military use of atomic power deserve the greatest consideration from every one capable of thought. The danger that an irrecoverable part of the patrimony of the human race may be wasted in blithe, though apparently peaceful and innocent extravagance, though less immediate, puts an equal moral responsibility upon mankind.

HENRY NORRIS RUSSELL
Princeton, N. J., January 7, 1946

PREFACE

Half a century ago, in the year 1896, the French physicist *Henri Becquerel* noticed that a piece of uranium mineral, which he had left in his desk drawer, caused the blackening of a pack of photographic plates which were resting in the same drawer. This peculiar property of uranium, and some other heavy chemical elements, to emit a radiation which could penetrate through the cardboard box containing the plates and the black paper in which they were wrapped, received the name of radioactivity and thus was started a new chapter in the science of physics.

In 1945, the radiation of uranium, flowing at a "somewhat faster" rate than in Professor Becquerel's desk drawer, burned and obliterated a good part of two Japanese cities, and now the spectre of the "atomic bomb" hangs heavily over humanity, threatening its complete destruction in case of another armed conflict between the major powers.

On the more cheerful side, the newly discovered possibility of liberating the hidden energy of uranium atoms promises us an almost unbelievable technical progress in the years to come. We may speak confidently about the miraculous "K-ration" fuels, a small package of which will be enough to fly a huge passenger airliner across the ocean. We may also prepare ourselves for a trip to the moon and to various planets of our solar system in a comfortable rocket-ship driven by atomic power.

It must be remembered, though, that the energy of uranium atoms which is now opened to our uses represents only a tiny drop in the immense reservoirs of atomic energy of the Universe, energy which is not any closer to our hands after the atomic-bomb experiment than it was before. Only the sun and stars at present have access to these main deposits of atomic fuel using them for more peaceful purposes of supplying light and warmth to the world.

In the present book we shall try to give a complete and consistent picture of the problem of atomic energy, and to answer the questions: what is it? where did it come from? and how can it be used for better or worse?

Since it is desired to present to the reader as complete a picture of the atomic-energy problem as possible, it is necessary to include some discussions which are intrinsically more complicated than others. In these cases the author attempted to help the understanding of the topic by schematic drawings of various nuclear processes which underline the main points of the discussion. There are also a number of pictures which the author drew simply as the relaxation in the process of writing the book; it is hoped that these pictures will also give some relaxation to those who will read it.

It may be added in conclusion that while an attempt has been made to include in the book everything important of what is known on the subject, the book does not contain any information of a confidential or secret nature, being based exclusively on existing scientific literature, and the facts concerning the technical production and utilization of atomic explosives officially released by the War Department of the United States Government.

It is the author's pleasant duty to express his thanks to Professor H. N. Russell for his kindness in reading the manuscript and making several valuable suggestions concerning the text.

G. GAMOW
The George Washington University
Washington, D. C.

September, 1945.

ATOMIC ENERGY

I. MODERN ALCHEMY

1. *Introduction. Chemical Energy.*

When a primitive man first rubbed two pieces of dry wood against each other, and little tongues of yellowish flame jumped out and started to consume small patches of moss and dry leaves which he placed around it, he made a discovery which was destined to weigh heavily on the entire subsequent history of the human race. By starting a fire the man learned how to liberate, at will, the energy, which is now known as the energy of chemical transformation; he could now control and use for his own purposes the phenomenon of fire which was previously familiar to him only in the form of catastrophic events of nature—roaring forest fires from which both men and animals ran in terror of their lives.

Fire was good for warming men's dwellings in the chilly winter nights, and for turning tough pieces of meat and plants into tasty food. It was also good for destroying the dwellings and the primitive wooden fortifications of the enemy in the continual series of conflicts between different groups of humanity. It was however much later that men learned how to turn the energy liberated in chemical reactions into the mechanical energy of motion, and ironically enough the first step in this direction was made for destructive rather than for constructive purposes.

In the middle of the thirteenth century the learned monk Roger Bacon announced his discovery that a mixture of saltpeter, charcoal, and sulphur gives a rapidly burning material, which can be used with success for propelling heavy shells at enemy ships and fortifications. And in the centuries following the discovery of gunpowder, wooden ships equipped with guns of varying caliber sailed the seven seas and shot it out with one another; the ships themselves, however, were propelled by the old-fashioned force of wind.

Towards the end of the seventeenth century a way was found to use the energy of fire to do mechanical work by turning water into steam and using this steam to push the piston in a primitive steam-engine. Still another two centuries had to elapse before it was learned that the energy liberated in burning can be used directly, without the intermediary of water and steam, by igniting a mixture of pulverized liquid fuels and air, in the cylinders of what is now known as an internal combustion engine.

At about the same time it was found that there are certain chemical compounds, containing in their structure both carbon and oxygen, in which chemical reactions leading to the liberation of energy occur so quickly that the entire transformation process can be considered as being practically instantaneous. Such rapid chemical transformations, usually known as explosions, result in terrific local pressures, and, instead of a more or less gentle push given to the piston in a gasoline motor by comparatively slow-burning inflammable mixtures, they tear apart their enclosure along with everything which happens to be in their immediate neighborhood. It is hardly necessary to say that high explosive materials, though useful in peaceful mining and road-building work, find their main application in the solution of military conflicts.

In looking through the entire history of human civilization we find that it is almost exclusively based on the utilization of the energy liberated in chemical transformations, or to be more specific, in a particular chemical transformation in which carbon, from dry wood, coal, or oil unites with the oxygen of the air to form the carbon-dioxide-gas which is the product of burning.

Step by step with the development of methods for the practical utilization of the energy liberated in chemical transformations, went the progress of our understanding of the intrinsic nature of these processes, and their connection with the general problem of the structure of matter. Every piece of matter, homogeneous as it may look at first sight, is actually built up of an immense number of almost unbelievably small particles known as *atoms*.

The atoms of different chemical elements unite to form atomic clusters of varying complexity, which represent constituent particles or *molecules* of various chemical compounds. Thus, for example, the union of one sodium atom and one chlorine atom forms a molecule of ordinary table salt; one atom of oxygen and two of hydrogen make a water molecule; eight carbons and eighteen hydrogens lead to a molecule of octane-gasoline; whereas three carbon atoms, five hydrogens, three nitrogens and nine oxygens arranged in the proper way give us a molecule of the highly explosive substance known as nitroglycerine which forms the main component of dynamite.

Chemical reactions leading to the transformation of one chemical compound into another must be considered as the result of the redistribution and rearrangement of the atoms forming the molecules of original substances into new cluster-formations representing the molecules of the reaction products.

Some chemical transformations, as for example, the formation of hydrogen peroxide, are connected with the absorption of energy and occur only if energy is constantly supplied from outside; they are known as *endothermic reactions*.

Other transformations, such as the oxidation of iron, burning of coal, or the explosion of dynamite, are *exothermic;* they liberate the internal energy of the molecules and can be used as the sources of chemical energy for technical purposes.

When a piece of coal is heated to a sufficiently high temperature, carbon atoms from its surface begin to unite with

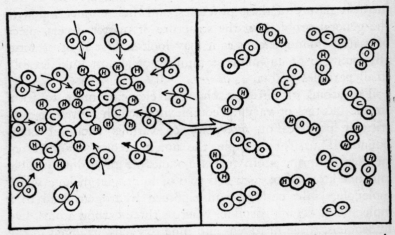

Fig. 1. The chemical reaction of oxidation of trimethylpentane, or in plain language, the burning of octane gasoline. The molecules of oxygen, formed of two oxygen atoms each, are attacking the molecule of gasoline made out of eight carbon and eighteen hydrogen atoms. The gasoline molecule is finally broken up and the oxygen atoms uniting with carbon and hydrogen atoms form the molecules of carbondioxide and water. This molecular transformation is connected with a large liberation of energy due to the strong affinity of oxygen for carbon and hydrogen.

oxygen atoms from the air, thus producing the heat liberated by this reaction. The process is, however, comparatively slow since it takes place only on the surface where carbon atoms come in contact with atmospheric oxygen. In the cylinder of a gasoline motor where the fuel is finely pulverized and mixed with air, we have essentially the same process, but a much speedier one since pulverized material has a much

larger contact surface with the air. In the case of gasoline
burning we also have not only the oxidation of carbon atoms,
but also the oxidation of hydrogen atoms contained in the
gasoline molecule.

A schematic picture of how a molecule of octane gasoline

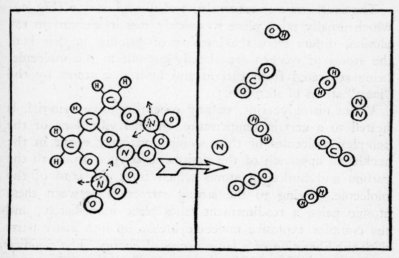

Fig. 2. The exothermal decomposition of a metastable molecule of gly-
ceryl trinitrate, or in plain language, the explosion of Nitroglycerine. Strong
thermal vibrations bring the atoms of oxygen (previously isolated by nitrogen atoms) close to the atoms of carbon and hydrogen, the result of which
is the breaking up of the entire molecule and the liberation of internal
energy.

unites with oxygen forming carbondioxide and water-vapor
is given in Fig. 1. When a molecule of gasoline encounters
the molecules of atmospheric oxygen (made of two oxygen
atoms each), an exothermic redistribution of atomic clustering must take place, since the attractive forces, or, as the
chemists say, "affinity" between oxygen atoms and the atoms
of carbon and hydrogen are stronger than the forces between
either two oxygens, two carbons, or carbon and hydrogen.

Thus, as a result of the collisions between oxygen molecules and the gasoline molecules, the old atomic bonds snap loose, new bonds are established, and the transformation into carbondioxide and water (in form of vapor) will take place with the liberation of molecular energy.

The exothermic transformation of nitroglycerine (Fig. 2), which usually takes place so quickly that it leads to an explosion, differs from the burning of gasoline in that here the atoms of oxygen are already present in the molecule, being separated from carbon and hydrogen atoms by the "inert" atoms of nitrogen.

When nitroglycerine, or any other explosive material, is heated to a certain temperature, thermal vibrations of the complex molecules of these compounds may result in the accidental approach of the peripheric oxygen atoms to the carbon and hydrogen atoms which form the core of the molecule. Owing to the strong attraction between these atomic pairs, a readjustment takes place immediately, and the complex explosive molecule breaks up into many parts with the liberation of a large excess of energy. The rapidity of transformation which makes us classify this reaction as an explosion rather than burning is due to the fact that both kinds of atoms necessary for the reaction are already present within the same molecule, so that practically no time is needed to bring them together.

It must be particularly emphasized here that the difference between burning and explosion lies not in the amount of energy liberated but in the rapidity with which such a liberation takes place. In fact, the burning of octane gasoline mixed with the necessary amount of oxygen liberates 2500 calories per gram of mixture as compared with only *1000* calories *

---

* The *calory* is a unit of heat energy which is equal to the amount of heat necessary to raise the temperature of one gram of water by one degree centigrade.

liberated per gram in the explosion of TNT. On the other hand the burning of a gasoline-air mixture in the cylinder of an automobile engine takes about one-tenth of a second, whereas in an explosion of TNT everything is over in only a few micro-seconds (a millionth part of a second).

In regard to energy liberation of chemical reactions, it may be noticed that although the amount of chemical energy varies from reaction to reaction, these variations are not very large, and it can be assumed that an average efficient chemical reaction liberates a few thousand calories per gram, i.e., the amount of energy which is necessary to bring to the boiling point an amount of cold water about ten times larger than the amount of fuel used.

Before we leave the subject of chemical transformations and the liberation of chemical energy, it is essential to discuss one question which has a close bearing on the problem of initiating and controlling molecular as well as atomic reactions.

We know that a piece of coal will not burn in the air, or for that matter even in pure oxygen, unless its temperature is brought up to the ignition point. Neither will an ordinary explosive explode unless we produce a sufficiently strong perturbation of its molecular structure either by heating it or by subjecting it to a powerful mechanical impact.

In general, *whenever we wish to start the liberation of chemical energy, we must first supply some energy in order to get the transformation going;* the existence of such a trigger mechanism is, of course, a necessary condition for making any practical use of exothermic chemical substances, since we do not wish to have fuels and explosives which would burn or go off the very minute that we produce them.

The property of any system loaded with energy which will be set free only after a certain small payment of energy is made from outside is known generally under the name of *metastability*.

In order to understand this important concept, suppose, for example, that we pour a large quantity of water into a deep hole in the ground (Fig. 3a). If no external work is done to extract this water from the hole, it will remain there indefinitely and will never get out by itself. There is also apparently no chance to make any mechanical use of such a

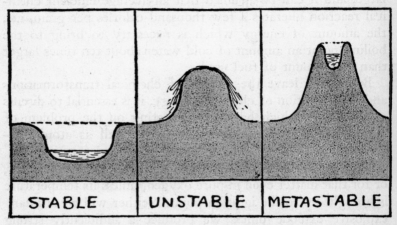

STABLE   UNSTABLE   METASTABLE

Fig. 3. Mechanical interpretation of the notion of stable, unstable and metastable states.

body of water, such as getting energy out of it for a hydro-electric station. We say that the water in such a hole is in *a stable state* of equilibrium.

If on the contrary, instead of pouring water into a hole we pour it on the top of a sugar loaf mountain (Fig. 3b), it will not stay there at all and will at once come down in a stream on both sides. The position of water on the top of such a mountain is *unstable* and can never be realized in practice.

Let us now consider the water filling a crater of an old

volcano (Fig. 3c). If left to itself, the water will stay there just as long as in the hole in the ground, although in principle much energy can be obtained from it by bringing it to a lower level. In order to get this energy we need, however, to bring the water over the rim of the crater, supplying for this purpose a certain amount of energy from the outside. Once over the rim, the water will cascade down the slope, and much more energy can be obtained from it than we put in to start it going. We say that the water in the crater was in a *metastable* state, and call the amount of energy which must be spent to bring it over the rim the *activation energy* pertaining to this particular case. It goes without saying that the activation energy of a given metastable state is always smaller than the total energy liberation of the expected final process, so that the advance payment in energy necessary to discharge a metastable state is always overcompensated by the final energy released. It may be also added that when we say, in ordinary conversation, that something is unstable, we should, properly speaking, use the more scientific term: "metastable." In fact, a stone which rolls down a hill un-assisted is in a truly unstable position; whereas a stone which will roll down when given only a slight push is actually in a metastable state of equilibrium, the strength of the necessary push measuring in this case the "activation energy" of the push-over process.

Now it must be clear to the reader how the notion of stability and metastability is used by chemists in respect to various chemical transformations. Water, for example, is a stable substance since in a water molecule oxygen and hydro-gen atoms are bound in the strongest possible way so that no energy can be obtained by any possible rearrangement. On the other hand nitroglycerine or a gasoline-oxygen-mix-ture are metastable substances, and are subject to the process of atomic rearrangement with the liberation of molecular binding energy. However such a rearrangement will start only if the molecules of these substances receive sufficient energy from outside in order to be able to go "over the top." These necessary amounts of activation energy are supplied in most cases by raising the temperature of the substance and thus increasing the intensity of thermal motion of its molecules. The increasing violence of intermolecular collisions leads to strong internal vibrations of individual metastable molecules (as in nitroglycerine) and also to their deeper penetration into each other's structure at the moment of collision, which facilitates the necessary internal rearrangement of atoms and the subsequent liberation of chemical binding energy.

In looking around for metastable substances from which chemical energy can be obtained, we find that practically all chemical compounds forming the crust of the earth are already in the state of stable equilibrium, and are in this respect completely useless as potential sources of energy. The only metastable materials found on the earth capable of producing energy are coal and oil, on the use of which our present human civilization is completely based. But coal and oil cannot be properly considered as regular minerals, and represent oddities of nature which humanity inherited by sheer luck from past geological epochs. It was indeed sheer luck that at a certain geological epoch, conditions on the surface of the earth were such that fallen dead trees were submerged in shallow waters, being thus prevented from the slow oxidation (or rotting) process which would inevitably result in their complete transformation into carbondioxide gas of the atmosphere. Since the fallen trees of the carboniferous era were separated from the atmospheric oxygen first by a layer of water, and later by various geological deposits which accumulated on top of them, we now have our chance to dig up the coal or pump out the oil into which they were transformed; thus we can obtain the energy by

starting the reaction with the atmospheric air from which
these materials were separated by unfavorable circumstances
for so many millions of years. But the deposits of coal and
oil, given to us by good providence, are limited, and with the
increasing demands for energy to feed our ever growing
technical development, it is quite reasonable to raise the
question: What sources of energy can be used when the deposits of coal and oil are exhausted?

Of course one could burn trees which grow under the rays
of sun all the time, or use the power of rivers and waterfalls
which is again the result of solar heat, or finally use the
energy of the sun directly by collecting sun-rays through
some arrangement of giant mirrors. But this would scarcely
satisfy the demands of humanity which, like a spendthrift
heir, is squandering the energy of coal and oil which
thoughtful nature accumulated and saved for us during the
period of over a hundred million years!

Into this sad picture of rapidly disappearing chemical
sources of energy now comes a new ray of hope, and the
vision of new and potentially unlimited sources of energy
hidden deep in the interior of the atom. In fact in the period
of only half a century since the discovery of radioactivity
gave us the first glimpse into the interior of the atom, the
power of the human brain has brought us to the possibility of
utilizing for our own purposes the immense potentialities of
atomic energy which heretofore was used exclusively only by
the sun and other stars in the Universe.

2. *The breaking of the Atom.*

In the previous section we gave a short survey of the generally known facts concerning molecular transformations and
the liberation of chemical energy, mostly with the purpose of
reminding the reader that in all chemical processes the atoms
of different elements stubbornly retain their own individ-

uality. They can be moved about as the figures in a complicated chemical chess-game, collected in various strategic
molecular configurations, or be again dispersed all over the
field. However, in all these moves, the atoms of oxygen remain atoms of oxygen and the atoms of iron remain atoms of
iron. It looks as though they are the truly elementary indivisible particles as implied by the name given to them by
Democritus in ancient Greece.

However, towards the beginning of the present century it
became clear that the atoms of various chemical elements
must possess a rather complicated internal structure, and be
formed of a large number of positive and negative electric
charges. In the processes of electric discharge, electric forces
can extract these negative charges, or electrons, from the inside of different atoms, leaving behind the positively charged
residues known as ions. The positive charges, however, cannot be extracted in this simple way, being evidently connected more intimately with the main mass of the atom.

According to the generally accepted atomic model, developed by Rutherford and Bohr on the eve of the first
world war, each atom of the different chemical elements consists of a heavy central nucleus with which the positive
charge of the atom is closely associated, and a swarm of negative electrons rotating around the nucleus held by the
force of electric attraction between the charges (Fig. 4).
The number of these atomic electrons, which is equal to the
positive charge of the nucleus, varies from element to element
and determines their chemical properties and their position
(atomic number) in the periodic system of elements. Thus a
hydrogen atom has only one electron; a helium atom—two;
a lithium atom—three; an iron atom—twenty-six; and so on
through the elements up to uranium which has ninety-two
electrons. The atomic electrons are responsible for the binding of various atoms together into the complex molecules of

various chemical compounds, and for the character of light emitted by different brands of atoms.

In the above description of atomic and molecular structure, atomic nuclei play the role of heavy inert bodies serving only as a kind of pivot point for the rotational motion of atomic electrons. On the basis of purely chemical and optical information one could easily assume that although the atoms themselves possess an internal structure, their nuclei represent those elementary and indivisible particles which Democritus

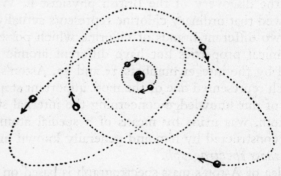

Fig. 4. The Rutherford-Bohr model of a carbon atom. Six electrons are circling around the heavy nucleus which is carrying six elementary units of positive electric charge. These so-called orbital electrons are responsible for hooking various atoms together into atomic clusters known as molecules.

originally had in mind. If this were so, the worst one could do to an atom would be to ironize it, by taking out several orbital electrons (which however would immediately jump back to their places as soon as one let them go), and the transformation of one element into another would be impossible.

We know now that this is not true. As early as in the middle of the last century the French chemist Prout tried to prove that the atoms of different chemical elements have a common nature, representing only various degrees of concentration of the atoms of hydrogen. Prout based his hypothesis on the fact that atomic weights of various elements are integers of the atomic weight of hydrogen, a rule which, at that time had been proved to hold quite generally, with only few exceptions. However, in science the popular saying that "the exception proves the rule" is not very applicable, and the fact that the chemically determined atomic weight of chlorine was 35.5 prevented, for more than half a century, the recognition of Prout's idea.

It was in 1919 that Prout's hypothesis came back to light, through the discovery of the British physicist F. W. Aston who showed that ordinary chlorine represents actually a mixture of two different brands of chlorine which possess identical chemical properties but have different atomic weights expressed by the integer numbers 35 and 37. Aston's discovery, which represented one of the most important steps in the progress of our knowledge concerning the internal structure of the atom, was made by means of a special atom-sorting machine constructed by him and generally known under the name of *mass spectrograph*.

The idea of Aston's mass spectrograph is based on sending a beam of electrically charged atoms, or ions as we usually call them, through an electric field formed between two plates of a plane condensor, and observing the deflection of the beam caused by the action of this field on the electric charges of flying atoms (Fig. 5). Since under the action of the same force, lighter atoms will be more strongly deflected from their original track than heavier ones, this kind of arrangement permits the sorting of atoms of a given substance according to their masses. Sending atoms of chlorine through his mass spectrograph, Aston noticed that no atoms at all came to the spot on the photographic plate where atoms of the mass 35.5 should have landed. On the contrary about 75 per cent of the chlorine atoms came to the spot corresponding to the mass 35 and about 25 per cent to the spot corresponding

to the mass 37. This proved beyond any doubt that ordinary
chlorine is a mixture of two chemically identical substances
or two *isotopes* as they are usually called. A mixture of 75 per
cent of the heavier isotopes and 25 per cent of the lighter
ones should give the mean atomic weight of 0.25 x 37 + 0.75
x 35 = 35.5 which is in excellent agreement with the chemical estimates.

The further study of various chemical elements by means

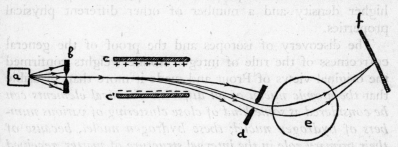

Fig. 5. The scheme of Aston's mass spectrograph. A bundle of positive
ions of the material under the investigation formed in the ion-source *a* is
cut by the diaphragm *b* into a narrow beam which is passed between the
plates of an electric condenser *cc'*. Since different atomic masses are deflected differently by the given electric field, only the ions of one definite
mass are passed by the second slit *d*. After the passage through the slit,
the ions are focused by the magnet *e* into one point on the photographic
plate *f*.

of Aston's mass spectrograph revealed the striking fact that
most of them represent a mixture of two or more isotopes
although in many cases only one of the isotopes is present in
large quantities. Thus carbon, which has the chemical atomic
weight 12, contains about one per cent of heavier isotopes
with atomic weight 13, whereas oxygen, usually known as
the element with atomic weight 16, has an admixture of two
heavier isotopes: 0.03 per cent of oxygen 17 and 0.17 per
cent of oxygen 18.

An extremely interesting discovery was made in 1932 by

the American chemist H. Urey, who showed that ordinary hydrogen contains about 0.02 per cent of heavier isotope with atomic weight 2, or *deuterium*, as it is now called, and he was able to separate this heavy water from ordinary water by the method of fractional distillation. Heavy water, in the molecules of which the atoms of ordinary hydrogen are replaced by atoms of deuterium, is identical with ordinary water in all chemical properties, except that it possesses a higher density and a number of other different physical properties.

The discovery of isotopes and the proof of the general correctness of the rule of integer atomic weights confirmed the original views of Prout and made it more than plausible that *the atomic nuclei of all different chemical elements can be considered as some kind of close clustering of various numbers of hydrogen nuclei; these hydrogen nuclei, because of their primary role in the internal structure of matter, received the special name of "protons."* However, final proof of the fact that protons enter into the structure of more complex atomic nuclei was given by Lord Rutherford, who, in his classical experiment on the artificial transformation of elements, succeeded, in 1919, in kicking protons out of the nuclei of different light elements by subjecting them to an intensive atomic bombardment.

Rutherford was well aware of the fact that in order to break up an ordinarily stable atomic nucleus, such as, for example, a nucleus of nitrogen, or aluminum, it is necessary to hit it very hard, and that the best atomic projectiles which could be used for such purpose can be found in the high-speed fragments ejected by the nuclei of unstable radioactive elements in the process of their spontaneous disintegration.

These fragments, known as *alpha-particles*, are thrown from decaying radioactive atoms with speeds of over ten thousand kilometers per second and have been shown to be nothing else but the nuclei of ordinary helium atoms which have lost their two electrons. Directing a beam of such alpha-particles on the targets formed by thin layers of various elements, Rutherford was able to notice a large number of protons which were apparently kicked out from the nuclei of these elements by the violence of the alpha-particles' impact. Figure 6 gives a schematic presentation of one of the first

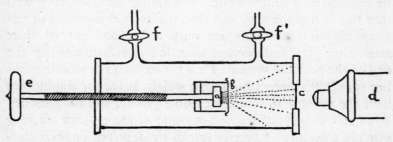

Fig. 6. Rutherford's apparatus for studying artificial transformation of elements under the action of alpha-bombardment. Alpha rays from a thin layer of radioactive material deposited on the front face of the metal plate *a* fall on a thin foil *b* of the material to be bombarded. The protons kicked out of the nuclei of the bombarded material fall on the fluorescent screen *c* and produce scintillations which can be observed through the microscope *d*. By turning the micrometric screw *e* one can bring the bombarded foil closer to or farther from the screen, thus measuring the maximum distance (the range) which the protons can go through the air. From the observed range of protons their energy can be easily calculated.

arrangements used by Rutherford for observing artificial transformation of various substances under the action of alpha bombardment.

The fact that protons are kicked out from the nuclei of different elements proves, of course, that they form an important part of nuclear structure, but does not necessarily mean that the complex nuclei are constructed entirely of protons, and if we assume for a moment such a point of view we shall immediately come into contradiction with the known facts about the masses and electric charges of the nuclei of different elements. In fact, in such a case the number of protons would be equal to the atomic weight of the element in question (16 protons in oxygen nucleus, and 35 and 37 protons respectively in the nuclei of two chlorine isotopes), and since each proton carries one positive electric charge, the total charge of the nucleus, or its atomic number, should then be equal to its atomic weight. We know, however, very well that this is not the case and that the atomic numbers of various chemical elements are only about one-half of their atomic weights, and become even less than half towards the end of the periodic system. Thus for oxygen the atomic number is only 8 whereas its atomic weight is 16, for sulphur we have the ratio of 16 to 32, for iron 26 to 54, and for mercury 80 to 200. It *looks as if about one-half of the protons entering into the structure of heavier nuclei are deprived of their electric charge* thus contributing only to the mass of the nucleus. The existence of such uncharged protons, or *neutrons* as they are now called, was suspected by Rutherford as early as in 1920, and a series of special experiments was put on in his laboratory in Cambridge in order to prove their existence by kicking them out of some nucleus. However, these experiments did not lead to any definite result, and the existence of neutrons was established only twelve years later as the result of the study of a mysterious new radiation which, according to the German physicist W. Bothe, was emitted from the atoms of beryllium under the action of alpha bombardment. This radiation, which was first mistaken for short electromagnetic waves, or "gamma-rays," emitted by the excited beryllium nuclei, was studied further in France by I. Curie and F. Joliot, who were able to show that it possesses the peculiar property of communicating high velocities to the atoms of the gas through which it passes, but who failed to understand its real nature.

It was only in the next year that J. Chadwick, the closest pupil of Lord Rutherford, succeeded in proving beyond any doubt that the radiation of beryllium represents actually a

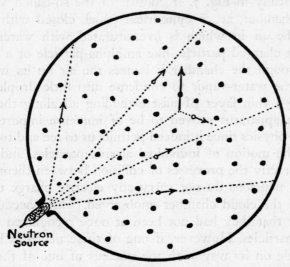

Fig. 7. A schematic presentation of the way in which neutrons are observed in a Wilson cloud chamber. A source of neutrons formed by a mixture of beryllium and radium in a sealed glass tube is placed through the opening in the wall of the chamber. Flying through the chamber the neutrons (white circles) have only a small chance to collide with the nuclei (black dots) of the atoms in the gas which fill the chamber, and thus escape unobserved. However, if such a collision takes place (as is shown in the figure), the nucleus struck by the neutron obtains a high velocity, and its trajectory becomes visible because of the ionization it produces. We can now find the track of the neutron by drawing a straight line from the neutron source to the point of collision.

beam of fast-moving electrically neutral particles which are exactly similar to ordinary protons except for the complete absence of the electric charge. When these fast particles move through matter they will from time to time collide with the atoms which happen to be in their way, communicating to them, by the force of direct mechanical impact, the high velocities observed by Curie and Joliot. The apparatus which served for the discovery and first study of neutrons is shown schematically in Fig. 7. It consists of the so-called Wilson's cloud chamber, i.e., a cylindrical vessel, closed with a glass plate, the air in which is oversaturated with water-vapor. When a charged particle, like an alpha-particle or a proton, flies through the chamber it ionizes the air on its way and causes the water-vapor to condense into little droplets thus forming a thin layer of mist extending all along the track. Such an apparatus proved to be of immense importance in modern physics since it indeed permits us to see and to photograph the motion of individual atomic particles, and to observe directly the processes of collision between them.

Since neutrons do not carry any electric charge they go through the cloud chamber unobserved, which accounts for the fact that they had not been at once recognized as individual particles. However, if one of these neutrons happens to collide on its way with the nucleus of one of the atoms forming the gas in the chamber, the nucleus will be kicked forward at high speed and its track will be clearly visible due to the layer of fog formed along it. Connecting the point at which the source of neutrons is placed, with the beginning of the track of the kicked nucleus, we find the trajectory of the otherwise invisible neutron. It may be added here that the collisions between neutrons and atomic nuclei which they encounter on their way follow exactly the laws of mechanical collision between two elastic spheres (except in cases when nuclear reaction takes place), so that observing the motion of the nucleus kicked by the neutron we can get all the information we want concerning the direction of motion and the speed of the neutron prior to the collision.

The discovery of neutrons filled up the missing link in the problem of the constituent particles forming complex atomic nuclei of different chemical elements, and removed the contradiction involved in trying to build the nuclei entirely of protons. It is clear now that the nuclei are built approximately half and half from protons and neutrons, the number of protons being determined by the atomic number of the element in question, and the number of neutrons by the difference between its atomic weight (which gives the total number of particles) and its atomic number. Thus the oxygen-nucleus with the charge 8 and mass 16 has in its structure eight protons and 16-8, i.e., also 8 neutrons, whereas the nucleus of iron has 26 protons and 54-26, i.e., 28 neutrons. Finally, the nucleus of the heaviest naturally existing element uranium, with atomic number 92 and atomic weight 238, contains in its structure 92 protons and $238 - 92 = 146$ neutrons.

It must be mentioned in concluding this section that neutrons do not represent a new kind of particle entirely different from protons, being, in fact, simply ordinary protons temporarily deprived of their electric charge. We know indeed quite a number of cases where a proton turns into a neutron by losing its electric charge, or, on the contrary, when a neutron becomes a proton by acquiring the necessary electric charge from outside. That is why, in modern nuclear physics, one prefers to introduce a new term *nucleon* as a collective description of the basic particles from which all nuclei are built, and to speak about protons and neutrons as charged and neutral nucleons.

The above stated fact that about one-half of the nuclear particles are protons and the other half neutrons, results from certain conditions of internal equilibrium of the nucleus which determine how many nucleons must be neutral and how many must be charged. If, as a result of some atomic reaction, a new nucleus is formed which contains too many neutrons or too many protons as compared with the relative number of these particles as required by a condition of equi-librium, a rearrangement of charges is bound to take place. If there are too many protons, some of them turn into neu-trons by ejecting their positive charges, which escape from the nucleus in the form of positive electrons. If, on the con-trary, the newly formed nucleus has too many neutrons, the reverse process takes place: surplus neutrons turn into pro-tons by emitting the negative electric charges in the form of ordinary negative electrons.

In our further study of various nuclear reactions we shall find a great many examples of such electric charge adjust-ments following the processes of nuclear transformation.

3. Energy better than gold.

Rutherford's discovery of the artificial transformation of elements gave reality to the ancient dream of medieval al-chemists who spent their entire lives in vain attempts to solve exactly that problem. But, whereas the alchemists of the past were mostly interested in the products of such transforma-tions and the possibility of making precious gold out of cheap metals, the interests of Modern Alchemy, as the science of transmutation of elements can be justly called, lie almost exclusively in the energy-liberation which accompanies such atomic transformation. In fact, it was realized almost from the first day of the discovery of radioactivity, that the energy liberated in various atomic transformations exceeds, by a fac-tor of many millions, the chemical energy which can be ob-tained from the same amount of material.

The prize of alchemical energy which lies hidden in the atomic nuclei of almost every substance can be estimated in tens of thousands of dollars per gram of material, so that if a way can be found to release that energy and make it work for us, the product of the transformation, even if it is pure gold, becomes quite unimportant.

Before going farther we must become thoroughly acquainted with the units in which energy is measured in physics, and particularly with the units which are used in expressing the energy liberations of atomic transformations.

A customary unit for measuring energy in physics is one *erg*, which can be defined as the kinetic energy of a mass of two grams moving with the velocity of one centimeter per second. It is not a very large unit in ordinary life: the kinetic energy of a ball in table-tennis play is measured in thousands of ergs, and on walking up steps to a third floor we use up several hundred billion ergs. But for individual atomic processes one erg is a very large unit, and here we have to use its smaller fractions such as a *micro-erg*, which is one millionth of one erg, or even a *micro-micro-erg* which is another million times smaller.

Chemical energies connected with the rearrangement of various atoms in molecules are most conveniently expressed in these smallest units: thus, for example, an atom of carbon uniting with two atoms of oxygen sets free 6.4 micro-micro-ergs of energy. In alchemic transformations, in which the energies involved exceed the chemical energies by millions, micro-ergs are used. When, as in the experiment described in the previous section, an alpha particle kicks out a proton from the nucleus of aluminum, the energy of the proton exceeds the energy of the incident alpha-particle by 3.7 micro-ergs. This represents the net energy gain of the reaction per one atom transformed. As we shall see later, some nuclear transformations result in still much larger energy liberations; thus the process of the so-called nuclear fission in which a nucleus of uranium breaks up spontaneously into two halves gives us 320 micro-ergs per nucleus.

If, however, you overheard a conversation between two nuclear physicists, especially the experimentalists, you would probably never hear expressions like micro-erg or micro-

micro-erg. They would speak about bombardment by "6 million-electron-volts protons" or "200 million-electron-volts energy-liberation." If you know something about electricity, this would sound strange to you since a "volt" is not the unit of energy but a unit of electric tension. The explanation lies in the fact that in experiments on atomic transformations one uses beams of charged atomic projectiles, accelerated to very high velocities in special electric high-tension machines, popularly known as *atom smashers,* which will be described in the following section. The word "volt" as used above simply refers to the accelerating potential used in these apparatus. To be exact, "one million-electron volts" is the energy communicated to a particle carrying one elementary electric charge, which was accelerated in a field of one million volts. This energy is known to be equal to 1.6 micro-ergs in ordinary units, so that "six million-electron-volts protons" are simply protons with the energy of $6 \times 1.6 = 9.6$ micro-ergs, and "200 million-electron-volts energy liberation" is the same as the energy liberation of $200 \times 1.6 = 320$ micro-ergs, referred to above in connection with the breaking up of a uranium nucleus. For short, one usually writes one million-electron-volt as MeV.

In the walls of the Cavendish Laboratory of Cambridge University where Rutherford performed his classical work on the transformation of atomic nuclei, this unit was also known under the name of "one crocodile." This amusing name was given by the students who worked in the laboratory with Lord Rutherford, because his famous loud voice and laughter, resounding down the corridors of the Cavendish, would warn them of his approach (giving them time to hide detective stories and restore order in the lab), just as in the story of the crocodile that swallowed a loud-ticking watch, the prospective victim was warned of its approach, (Fig. 8). Thus, MeV, the nuclear unit of energy which might have been called "one

Rutherford" became "one crocodile" to the students in the Cavendish.

We shall now see how nuclear transformation energies look if expressed not per single atom but per gram of the material used. Let us take as the first example the transformation of aluminum under the action of alpha-particle bombardment.

Fig. 8. Why one million electron volts was called a crocodile.

The atomic weight of aluminum is 27 or, expressed in grams, $27 \times 1.66.10^{-24} = 4.5.10^{-23}$ gm.* Thus one gram of pure aluminum contains $\dfrac{1}{4.5.10^{-23}} = 2.2 \times 10^{22}$ atoms. If every single atom is transformed giving (comp.p. . . .) 3.7 micro-ergs, the total energy liberation per gram will be 8.2 x 10^{22} micro-ergs or 6.10^{16} ergs.

* Here the figure $1.66.10^{-24}$ gm. represents the weight of one atom of hydrogen.

In a similar way we calculate that there are $2.5.10^{21}$ atoms in one gram of uranium which, with 320 micro-ergs per atom, gives us the total of 8.10^{23} micro-ergs or 8.10^{17} ergs. It is more convenient in such cases to use the unit of heat-energy known as *calory* which was previously defined as the heat which is necessary to raise the temperature of one gram of water by one degree centigrade. One often uses also *kilo-calories* which are one thousand times larger. One calory is known to be equal to $4.185.10^7$ ergs, which means that we need that many ergs of energy to heat a gram of water by one degree. One kilocalory correspondingly equals $4.185.10^{10}$ ergs. The energy, or heat, developed in ordinary chemical transformations can be very conveniently expressed in kilo-calories. Thus, for example, burning one gram of coal in atmospheric oxygen liberates about 8 kilocalories, whereas an explosion of TNT sets free instantaneously the energy of 1 kilocalory. Applying this unit to our nuclear transformations we find that *the complete transformation of aluminum and uranium will give a grand total of 1.4 and 19 millions kilo-calories respectively*. These numbers emphasize once more the terrific differences between the energy of chemical and alchemical transformations. In fact, the atomic energy concealed in only one gram of uranium is equal to that of 19 million grams or 19 tons of TNT!

4. *The nucleus as a fluid droplet.*

In order to understand the ways and means by which the energy lying deep in the interior of atomic nuclei can be released and utilized for our own purposes, we must first get a deeper insight into the detailed structure of that minute particle and learn more about the forces which hold it together or, on the contrary, lead to its break-up. It is clear that the forces which hold the nucleus in one piece cannot be of a purely electric nature, since one half of the nuclear particles, the neutrons, do not carry any electric charge, whereas the other half, the protons, are all positively charged, thus repelling one another and contributing to nuclear disruption rather than to its stability.

Thus in order to understand why the constituent parts of the nucleus stick closely together one must necessarily assume that there exists between them forces of some other kind, attractive in nature, which act on uncharged neutrons as well as on positively charged protons. Such forces which, irrespective of the nature of the particles involved, make them adhere are generally known in physics as "cohesive forces" and are encountered, for example, in ordinary liquids where they hold together the separate molecules and also lead to the familiar phenomenon of surface-tension.

It may be remembered that in the classical theory of liquids, which can be found in any elementary textbook of physics,

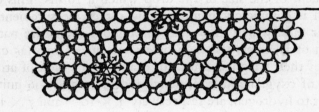

Fig. 9.

the phenomenon of surface tension is explained by an argument, illustrated graphically in Fig. 9. A particle which is deep inside a liquid is subjected to the attractive forces from other particles surrounding it on all sides, so that the total resultant of all these pulls is exactly zero. On the other hand, a particle located on the surface has all its neighbors only on one side, so that their combined attraction results in a strong force pulling the surface-particle inwards. Since every particle located on the surface is pulled inwards by other particles, the liquid will have a general tendency to reduce its free surface to the minimum possible, which explains the spherical shape assumed by any liquid drop which is not acted upon by any external forces. It is well known that a sphere is the geometrical figure which possesses the smallest surface for a given total volume.

The assumption that the forces acting between the constituent particles of an atomic nucleus are similar to those acting between the molecules of an ordinary liquid, led the present writer, in 1930, to formulate the *droplet-model* of an atomic nucleus according to which *different nuclei are considered as the minute droplets of a universal "nuclear fluid."*

The first important consequence of the *nuclear droplet* theory was the conclusion that the volumes of different atomic nuclei must be proportional to their weights, since the density of nuclear fluid must always remain the same independent of the size of the drop which it forms. This conclusion is completely confirmed by direct measurements of nuclear radii which show that throughout the entire natural system of elements the radii of atomic nuclei vary as cubic roots of their weights. Thus, for example, the radii of atomic nuclei of oxygen and lead, which weigh 16 and 206 units in respect to hydrogen, are respectively 3×10^{-13} and 7×10^{-13} centimeters, which is in complete agreement with the expected cubic-root proportion. Remembering that the actual weight of a hydrogen-atom * is $1.66.10^{-24}$ gm., we find that the nuclei of oxygen and lead weigh respectively 2.66×10^{-23} and 3.42×10^{-22} grams. Since the volumes corresponding to the above radii are 1.13×10^{-37} and 1.44×10^{-36} cubic centimeters we obtain in both cases the value of $2.4 \times 10^{14} \frac{\text{gm}}{\text{cm3}}$ for the density of nuclear fluid.

* or hydrogen nucleus, which is the same because the electrons being 1840 times lighter do not contribute much to the atomic mass.

This is truly a density which challenges our imagination! If the nuclear fluid which is dispersed through space in the form of minute droplets surrounded by very rarefied electronic envelopes could be collected to form a continuous material, one cubic centimeter of it would weigh two hundred and forty million tons.

Along with its almost unbelievably high density, nuclear fluid possesses a correspondingly high surface tension. It may

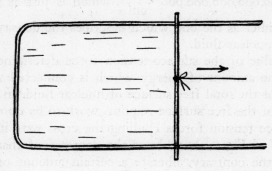

Fig. 10.

be remembered from the study of elementary physics that the surface tension of liquids is measured by the force acting on the unit length of the free surface boundary. Thus, for example, if we spread a soap-film in a square formed by a ⊏-shaped wire and piece of straight wire put across it in the way indicated in Fig. 10, the forces of surface tension will pull the cross-bar wire to the left trying to reduce the surface of the film. Measuring this total force, and dividing it by the length of the cross-wire, and also by the factor 2 because the soap film has two surfaces and consequently acts with double force, we arrive at the value of the surface-tension force acting on the unit length. The surface tension of water, for example, is known to be 75 dynes per cm., a dyne being the unit of force equal approximately to the weight of

one milligram (0.000035 ounces), whereas in mercury it is
$465 \dfrac{\text{dynes}}{\text{cm}2}.$

The surface tension of nuclear fluid, which is measured, of
course, not with the cross-wire arrangement shown in Fig.
10, but by the amount of electric energy which is necessary
to deform or break up a nuclear droplet, was found to be
93,000,000,000,000,000,000 $\dfrac{\text{dynes}}{\text{cm}}$ which is just as nice and
big a number as the one which describes the density of that
fantastic nuclear fluid.

The value of the surface-tension force determines immediately the amount of energy which is connected with any
changes of the total free surface of nuclear fluid. In fact any
increase of the free surface requires work to be done against
the surface tension forces (pulling the cross wire in the experiment of Fig. 10), whereas the decrease of that surface
will, on the contrary, liberate a certain amount of surface
energy. Numerically, the amount of energy per unit surface,
as expressed in ergs, is given by the same number as the surface-tension force * being equal to 93,000,000,000,000,000,000
ergs per square centimeter, so that in order to calculate the
total surface energy of a nucleus we have to multiply its surface by the above number.

Instead of expressing the surface energy per unit surface,
we can more conveniently express it per one nuclear particle
located on the surface. Since the diameter of a neutron or
proton is about $3.2.10^{-13}$ cm., each of them will occupy on
the nuclei surface an area of 10^{-25} cm^2., so that there would
be 10^{25} particles per square centimeter. Dividing the above

---

* This is, of course, not a coincidence, but is due to the fact that the surface energy can be determined as the product of the surface-tension force
acting on the length of one centimeter, multiplied by the displacement
which is in this case also one centimeter.

total surface energy by that number of particles we find that there is about 9.10^{-6} erg or about 5 crocodiles of energy per particle. This represents the energy which would be necessary to remove one nucleon from the surface of the nucleus against the forces of cohesion.

5. Nuclear stability and energy release.

In considering atomic nuclei of different chemical elements as minute droplets of a universal nuclear fluid which apart from its extremely high density and correspondingly strong surface forces must be rather similar to any ordinary liquid, we may expect that these nuclear droplets will behave in about the same way as the droplets of any other liquid. In observing droplets of, let us say, mercury rolling on the surface of a saucer we notice that whenever two such droplets meet, they will immediately fuse, forming a larger droplet.

The fusion of two droplets into one is the work of the surface tension forces which tend to reduce the total free surface of the liquid. In fact, it is easy to show that the surface of one big droplet is smaller than the combined surfaces of two half-size droplets. Since the total volume of the compound droplet is twice the volume of each of the smaller ones, its radius must be $\sqrt[3]{2} = 1.26$ times larger, and its surface $(1.26)^2 = 1.59$ times larger. Thus when two half-size droplets fuse into one, the total surface reduces in the ratio of 2 to 1.59 or by twenty percent. It is also not difficult to show by simple arithmetic that the same is true when two droplets are of different size, although in this case the relative decrease of the total surface is expressed by a smaller number. The fusion of two droplets with the mass ratio 3:1 reduces the surface by 19 per cent, whereas for the mass ratio 10:1 we have only 13 per cent reduction. Thus the fusion of two droplets into one always leads to the liberation of surface energy and takes place spontaneously whenever two droplets meet.

On the other hand, in order to break one droplet into two or more parts we have to supply energy from outside, as such a process would never happen without external influence. If the surface-tension forces were the only forces acting in the nucleus, all nuclei in the universe would gradually fuse together forming a large pool of the super-dense nuclear fluid.

The situation changes, however, quite considerably if we take into account that, apart from surface-tension forces, electric forces of repulsion are also present in the nuclei. In fact, in contrast to ordinary liquids, nuclear fluid is always electrically charged since about one half of its constituent particles are protons. The electric repulsion forces between the nuclear charges act in the opposite direction to the forces of surface tension, tending to prevent the fusion of any two droplets, and on the contrary tending to disrupt every small droplet into still smaller ones.

In order to understand the situation more clearly, let us consider a spherical droplet of nuclear fluid subjected to the action of surface-tension—as well as electric-repulsion forces (Fig. 11). As long as a droplet retains its spherical shape all forces are in balance. But if we deform our droplet, giving it a slightly elongated shape, the conflict between the two opposing forces immediately begins. The forces of surface tension will tend to return the nucleus to its original spherical shape, whereas the electric forces between the positive charges on the opposite extremities will try to increase the existing elongation and to break up the nucleus into two halves. The outcome of the struggle between the two opposing forces depends, of course, on their relative strength, which may be different in nuclei of different sizes.

To decide which side wins we have to compare the total energy of the original nucleus with the combined total energy of its two prospective halves. By total energy we mean here the combined energy of both surface tension and

electric forces. We have already seen above that the fission
of a nuclear droplet into two parts leads to an increase of
the surface-energy so that under the action of the surface-
tension alone it would never break up spontaneously.

What about the change of electric energy connected with
such fission? Everyone who has a little knowledge of electricity will remember that the electric energy of a charged

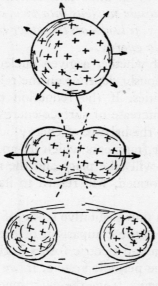

Fig. 11.

sphere is given by the square of its charge divided by its
radius. This law is quite general, and can be applied to the
charged droplets of nuclear fluid just as well as to the large
copper-spheres on a glass stand used in elementary experiments in electricity.

Let us use it now to calculate the change of electric energy
connected with the breaking of a nucleus into two halves,
with the electric charge distributed equally between them.

Since each of the two resultant droplets has now one half of the original charge, and their radii are 1.26 times smaller than that of the original droplet (comp. p. 31), the electric energy of each will be $(\frac{1}{2})^2 \times 1.26 = 0.315$ times that of the original big droplet. The combined electric energy of the two halves will be only 0.63 of the original value, representing a thirty-seven per cent reduction.

Thus we come to an important conclusion—that *whereas the fission of an atomic nucleus into two halves increases the total surface energy, it leads, on the other hand to a reduction of the total electric energy.*

The question of whether a given nucleus will or will not break up spontaneously depends on the relative values of the above two quantities. If the reduction of electric energy overbalances the increase of surface-energy, the nucleus will break up by itself, the balance of energy being communicated to the two nuclear fragments which fly apart. If the opposite is true, no fission will take place and the nucleus, no matter how strongly deformed, will return to its original spherical shape.

The last step in our qualitative study of the equilibrium of a nuclear droplet is the comparison of the relative values of the surface-tension and electric forces in the nuclei of different elements of the periodic system. If we proceed along the sequence of elements from the light nuclei to the heavier ones, the surface energy, which is determined by the total surface of the nucleus, increases comparatively slowly, being proportional to the $\frac{2}{3}$d power of atomic weight.* On the other hand, electric energy increases approximately as the square (or more exactly as $\frac{5}{3}$d power) of the nuclear charge which is in its turn roughly proportional to the atomic

---

* 2/3d power is the square of the cubic root. Thus if atomic weight increases by a factor of 8, the surface increases by a factor of $(\sqrt[3]{8})^2 = 2^2 = 4$.

weight. Thus the electric energy of the nucleus increases much faster with its weight than its surface energy, and whereas for light nuclei the conservative forces of surface tension may hold their field in making the nucleus stable, they will inevitably be subdued in the heavier elements by the electric repulsion forces whose tendency is to break up the nucleus into many pieces.

In their classical work on the general problems of nuclear stability, which was published in the fall of 1939, *N. Bohr* and *J. A. Wheeler* gave a detailed study of the balance of nuclear forces along the above described lines, and were able to predict the exact limit beyond which the disruption or fission of a nucleus must be expected to take place. It was determined that *the instability of atomic nuclei in respect to fission begins just about halfway up the periodic system of elements, approximately near the position of silver.* Thus the nuclei of all elements heavier than silver are principally unstable and, under the action of a sufficiently strong external excitation, would break up into two halves with the liberation of considerable amounts of internal energy. On the contrary, in the lighter nuclei the forces of surface-tension have the upper hand over the electric repulsion forces, so that we can expect the spontaneous fusion process whenever two light nuclei, with a combined weight less than that of silver, come close together. In Fig. 12 is shown the curve calculated by Bohr and Wheeler, which gives the energy-balance connected with the breaking up of atomic nuclei of various elements into two halves. We see that for the elements of the upper half of the periodic system the balance is positive, meaning that the process is connected with the liberation of nuclear energy. For the elements of the first half of the periodic system the curve goes below the zero-line, which means that in order to break up one of such nuclei we have to put in a certain amount of energy. In this region, not the fission but rather the fusion of the two nuclei will lead to the liberation of energy.

We thus come to an unexpected conclusion that *from the viewpoint of alchemical transformation, all chemical elements with the exception of silver * are in a metastable state, and can*

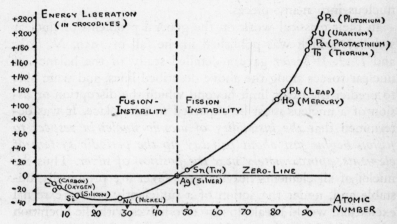

Fig. 12. Energy liberation connected with the breaking up of a nucleus into two equal parts. For all elements heavier than silver this energy is positive; this means that the fission of these elements takes place exothermically and can be used as an energy source. For the elements lighter than silver the energy is negative, and we have to use external work to break up the nucleus. This means, however, that the fusion of two light nuclei is an exothermic process.

liberate vast amounts of hidden internal energy either by fusing together (lighter elements), or by breaking up through the process of fission (heavier elements.) This result is in striking contrast with the situation in the realm of chemical transformations where, as we have seen in the beginning of this chapter, all molecular configurations are already in their

* Or some neighboring element, since the intersection of the curve in Fig. 12 with the zero line has not yet been exactly determined.

most stable state, the meager deposits of coal and oil representing the only remaining metastabilities from which chemical energy can be extracted.

We find now, however, that we live literally inside an alchemic powder-magazine where practically every substance, be it a glass of water, a slice of bread, or a piece of iron, is loaded with terrific amounts of energy which only await the chance to be liberated. The sun and all the other stars are using this hidden energy for supporting their eternal radiation of light and heat into surrounding space, and now, 3,000,-000,000 years after the creation of the universe, the uses of this energy are being developed for its own purposes, by a small but ambitious lump of organic matter on the surface of the Earth, which calls itself: man.

6. *Activation energies of nuclear reactions.*

If silver is the only stable element from the point of view of alchemic transformation, if the atoms of all the lighter elements have the tendency of fusing together until they become atoms of silver, and if all heavier elements could turn into silver through the process of nuclear fission, why then did this transformation not take place a long time ago? And why is the entire Universe not made out of pure silver? The answer to this question lies in the fact that atomic nuclei are not entirely unstable, which would, of course, lead to their immediate transformation into silver, but are in what we called before a metastable state which requires a certain amount of activation so that the transformation can take place. In fact, any two light nuclei will fuse together if they approach very closely to each other, *but* such a close approach is usually prevented by the electric repulsive forces between their positive charges. In the same way a metastable nucleus of a heavier element will break up into two halves if it is sufficiently deformed and set into vibration, say by a vigorous collision with another nucleus, *but* such violent collisions do not occur under the usual circumstances.

The situation here is identical to that existing in the case of a piece of wood which will not burn without being first heated, or a charge of a high explosive which will not detonate without being subjected to a powerful blow. However, in the case of chemical reactions the activation energies are sufficiently low, permitting us to achieve the desired result by comparatively simple means. Thus one can set dry wood afire (or, at least one says so) by vigorously rubbing two pieces against each other, and an explosive can be detonated by hitting it strongly enough with a hammer.

The low activation-energies of chemical transformations explain the fact that all the chemical compounds found in nature are already in their most stable state, so that no more energy can be obtained from them. It is true that we find coal and oil preserved by certain unusual circumstances, but nobody would even expect to discover natural deposits of, say, TNT which could be dug out and loaded directly into shells!

In the case of alchemically metastable substances the situation is entirely different, since along with tremendously large reaction-energies, they possess correspondingly high energies of activation. As we shall see in the next chapter, nuclei of various chemical elements were formed several billion years ago at the birth of the Universe, before the Earth or even the stars existed, and when physical conditions everywhere were entirely different from what they are now. The rapidly varying physical conditions of that early epoch, out of which finally came the Universe as we know it now, left various nuclei in metastable states which cannot be easily broken up under the considerably milder conditions of the present time. Only in the deep interior of the stars do the physical conditions approach the limits necessary for the incitation of al-

chemic reactions, but even in this case the temperatures are
only sufficient to cause a slow "alchemical burning" of but
a few of the lightest elements.

Thus the problem of producing atomic transformations on
a large scale is not an easy one, and puts man in competition
with the most fundamental forces of the cosmos. In this section we shall consider the problem of nuclear activation energies, i.e., the strength of the impact which is necessary to

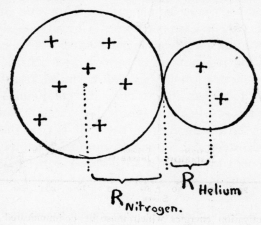

Fig. 13.

bring the nuclei of different elements out of their dormant
metastable states.

As stated before, the fusion of two light nuclei is usually
prevented by a strong repulsion between their positive electric charges. What should be the energy of impact between
such two nuclei in order to bring them into bodily contact in
spite of this strong repulsion? The question is simply an-
swered by reference to the law of potential energy between
two electric charges. It says that in order to bring two electric charges within a certain distance against the forces of
their mutual repulsion, we must supply energy equal to the

product of these charges divided by the distance. Thus, the
kinetic energy which two nuclei must have in order to come
surface to surface in the process of a head-on collision is equal
to the product of nuclear charges divided by their combined
radius (Fig. 13). Since the radii vary slightly from nucleus

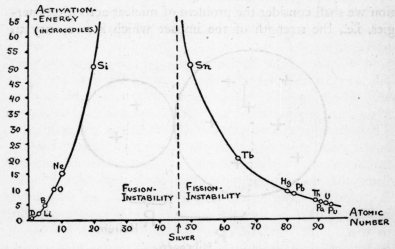

Fig. 14. Activation energies which must be communicated to atomic
nuclei to cause an exothermic transformation. For the first half of the periodic system we have the energy necessary to bring together two nuclei
against the electric repulsion (only the cases of two identical nuclei are
shown in the diagram). For the elements of the second part of the periodic
system, activation energies are the energies required to produce a critical
deformation.

to nucleus (being proportional to the cubic root of the
atomic weight), the main factor is given by the product of
the electric charges, so that the activation energies increase
very rapidly along the periodic system of elements. Thus for
a carbon-hydrogen collision the charge-factor is $6 \times 1 = 6$,
for nitrogen-helium, $7 \times 2 = 14$, and for a collision between
two oxygen nuclei, $8 \times 8 = 64$.

The smallest value of activation energy is, of course, obtained for the collision between two protons, or two deuterons, or a proton and a deuteron, since in these cases both charges are equal to unity.

In Fig. 14 the curve represents the activation energies for the fusion of two identical nuclei of different elements. It shows that in the case of two protons or two deuterons this energy is only about 0.5 crocodiles, increasing rapidly for heavier elements.

In the case of the elements of the second half of the periodic system, the term "activation-energy" refers to the energy which must be communicated to the metastable nucleus in order to produce the critical deformation leading to fission. These energies can be calculated on the basis of the droplet-model of an atomic nucleus, by taking into account the distorted balance between the forces of surface-tension and the forces of electric repulsion. The results, as calculated by *Bohr* and *Wheeler* in their fundamental work, are also shown in Fig. 14. We see that the situation here is exactly opposite to that in the previous case: activation-energies for fission being smallest at the end of the periodic system of elements, increase rapidly in the direction of smaller atomic weights. But even in the case of uranium, where the activation-energy is only 5 crocodiles, it is still considerably higher than the activation energy of only half a crocodile as in the case of two-deuteron-fusion.

Thus we come to a general conclusion that *the best opportunity for producing atomic transformations and liberating their hidden energy, lies on the two opposite ends of the periodic system.* It must be either the heavier isotope of hydrogen: deuterium, or the lighter isotope of uranium: * U-235,

---

* We shall see in Ch. III that uranium is formed essentially by two isotopes 238 and 235 in the proportion 99.3 and 0.7 percent, and that the lighter uranium isotope has the smallest activation energy for fission.

both of which are, unfortunately, extremely rare on the Earth.

7. *Quantum-leakage and Resonance*

In regard to the activation-energies characterizing the heights of the barriers of force which stand in the way of various nuclear transformations, we must discuss the extremely important phenomenon of the so-called *quantum-leakage* which in many cases reduces quite essentially the difficulties of penetration through such barriers. In order to understand the nature of this phenomenon, which plays a very important role in many branches of modern physics and especially in the field of the nuclear processes, the reader must have some knowledge of the general quantum-theory, the discussion of which is outside the scope of the present book. Thus, referring the reader to other books on that subject,* we shall here discuss the phenomenon of quantum-leakage only in a very general way.

In the first section of the present chapter we gave as an example of metastability a body of water filling the crater of an old volcano (Fig. 3). The water was said to be in a metastable state because a certain amount of work was necessary in order to bring it over the barrier formed by the walls of the volcano. Another possibility is, however, that the water would *leak* through the surrounding walls. Of course, everyone can understand *that*, but this kind of leakage, due to the porosity of the wall materials, represents only a helpful analogy for understanding the phenomenon of quantum-leakage discussed here. This quantum leakage has nothing to do with the porosity of the wall material and, in fact, nothing to do with material walls, since the barriers encountered in nuclear

* For example, the author's book: "Mr Tompkins in Wonderland." Cambridge University Press and Macmillan, 1940, in which the Dreams II and IV, as well as Lecture III are devoted entirely to that subject.

transformation are the barriers of force. When a proton approaches an atomic nucleus it is first repelled by the electric force, and only on much smaller distances does it encounter the attractive forces of cohesion which finally pull it in. Thus, in order to enter the nucleus, the proton must have a sufficiently high velocity to move against the repulsive electric forces and to reach the place where the attraction begins. If it does not have the necessary initial velocity, it will be stopped by the forces of repulsion somewhere halfway, and thrown back to the starting point. Thus the repulsive force forms something like a wall, or rather, a steep hill, which the proton must climb all the way to the top until it can happily roll down into the nuclear interior. It is the height of this figurative wall of force which is described by the term activation energy.

According to classical physics, and also to common sense, no object can move against forces which exceed its original energy of motion; and no one would believe that a stone gently thrown up by a child's hand could roll over the roof of the Empire State Building! However, both classical physics and common sense are slightly mistaken in this case, and we now know that such a phenomenon is really possible. However, the probability of its occurrence in everyday life is so negligibly small that it need not be considered. But, the smaller the size of the bodies involved, the larger the chance of penetration, and for the tiny particles like protons or alpha-particles which we encounter in the world of the atomic nucleus, quantum-leakage of the barriers is quite a common phenomenon. Even if the incident particle has much less energy than is necessary to get through, against the opposing electric forces, the leakage, though also small, will still not be zero, and at least some penetrations into the nucleus will take place. If, however, the energy of the particle is only a little smaller than the height of the barrier, a considerable penetration can be expected, and the incident particles will enter the nuclei as if the top of the barrier did not exist at all.

The application of this quantum-leakage theory to the problems of nuclear transformations caused by atomic bombardment was developed by the present writer in 1928, and led to the complete understanding of the basic *Rutherford* experiments on the artificial transformation of different elements bombarded by alpha-particles of varying energy. We shall see later that the phenomenon of quantum-leakage also plays a very important role in the problem of energy-production in stars, as well as in the discussion of various possibilities of the atomic-energy released by artificial methods.

Another important consequence of the quantum theory in application to the problems of nuclear transformation consists in the so-called phenomenon of *resonance*. This word is undoubtedly quite familiar to the reader and can be demonstrated in many elementary physical examples. Thus, a tuning fork, or a violin string, will respond to a sound, the frequency of which corresponds to its own vibrational frequency. In a similar way a radio-receiving set will work only if it is "tuned" to the frequency of the incident radio-waves.

In the field of nuclear transformations, resonance takes place when the energy of bombarding projectiles is equal to the reasonance-energy of the bombarded nucleus. Thus when the projectiles are too fast or too slow, their impact against the nucleus will have but little chance to produce the transformation, whereas if their velocity is exactly right the transformation will occur almost in each case. Later in this book we will encounter many examples where this quantum-resonance plays a very important role.

8. *Atomic Bombardment and its Disadvantages.*

At the time when Rutherford first succeeded in producing artificial transformation of light elements, the only high-energy projectiles suitable for that purpose were the natural alpha-particles ejected in the decay process of different radio-active substances. It was naturally desirable to devise methods by which one would be able to produce strong beams of atomic projectiles simply by accelerating various charged particles (ions) in strong electric fields. Apart from removing the necessity of using rare and expensive radioactive substances, such methods would indeed permit us to use other different types of atomic projectiles (such as, for example, protons), which, being sufficiently developed, could promise us projectiles possessing a higher energy than the fastest natural alpha particles of ordinary radioactive elements. The first successful attempt to produce a beam of atomic projectiles was due to *Cockroft* and *Walton* who, in the year 1932, built, in the Cavendish Laboratory, the first atomic accelerator or, as it is now called, *atom smasher*. Their arrangement was a comparatively simple one, and consisted of a number of electric condensers which were charged from a high-tension transformer, and then discharged simultaneously in a cascade fashion. Using a 350 kilovolt transformer, they were able to amplify it almost up to one million volts. Since the energies of natural alpha-particle range as high as eight million crocodiles, it was apparently uninteresting to use the transformer for producing beams of artificial alpha-rays. However, by filling the feeding-chamber of the apparatus with hydrogen instead of helium, one could obtain something much more interesting: a beam of high-energy protons which were expected to be much more efficient atomic projectiles than ordinary alpha-particles. In fact, since the charge of a proton is only one half of an alpha-particle's charge, the repulsive forces which it encounters in approaching the atomic nucleus are twice as small, so that in order to go over the top of the barrier surrounding the nucleus of a given element, protons required only half of the energy necessary for an alpha-particle. Since, however, in many cases the bombarding projectiles do not go *over* the barrier but rather through it, by virtue of the above discussed phenomenon of quantum-leakage, protons have still another advantage over alpha-particles. It can be shown that for equal heights of the barrier, and equal kinetic energy of incident particles, a lighter particle will "leak through" much more easily than a heavy one.

Thus, in spite of the fact that the energies used in the first experiments on proton bombardment were smaller than in the case of natural alpha-particles, the efficiency of the bombardment was about the same, and in some cases larger than in the old experiments. The first element broken up by proton bombardment was lithium, the nucleus of which, after capturing the incident proton, breaks into two parts, each of which is an alpha-particle. This process can be written symbolically as:

$$_3Li^7 + {}_1H^1 \rightarrow 2\ {}_2He^4$$

and is connected with the liberation of 17 crocodiles per lithium atom transformed. Similar processes have been observed in other light elements subjected to proton-bombardment. Thus sending a beam of proton on nitrogen we observe the reaction

$$_7N^{14} + {}_1H^1 \rightarrow {}_6C^{11} + {}_2He^4$$

which is an energy loss of 3.3 crocodiles, whereas in the case of boron we have a very interesting case of triple splitting:

$$_5B^{11} + {}_1H^1 \rightarrow 3\,{}_2He^4$$

with the liberation of 8.7 crocodiles of energy.

The subsequent development of experimental technique led to various new types of atom smashers, two of which we shall describe here in some detail. They are the electrostatic-generator, and cyclotron.

The electrostatic generator, first proposed by Van de Graff

(Fig. 15), is based on a classical principle according to which the electric charge communicated to a spherical conductor is immediately distributed on its surface.* The apparatus consists of a hollow metal sphere with an opening through which

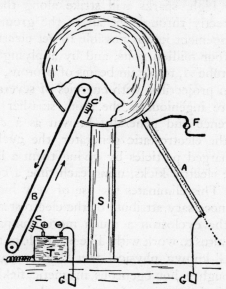

Fig. 15. The scheme of Van de Graff's electrostatic generator. T is the rectifying high-tension transformer, G the grounding, B the belt, S the insulating support of the spherical conductor, A the tube in which the acceleration of projectiles is taking place, F the feeding tube through which the ions of the material to be used for bombardment are brought in, and C, C' the combs depositing and collecting the electric charge.

passes a belt made of insulated material. When the belt runs around, being driven by a special motor, an electric charge is induced on it by an ordinary high-tension transformer, "T", and then delivered to the sphere as soon as the charged parts of the belt come in. As the belt runs round and round, more

* This is due to the mutual repulsion between the charges of the same sign.

and more electric charge is communicated to the sphere and its potential steadily rises to very high values. The limit of high potentials which can be obtained this way depends only on the insulation of the sphere: when the potential becomes too high, sparks will strike along the supporting beams or directly through the air to the ground. By using such an arrangement it was possible to get electric potentials of three or four million volts, and by applying them to the accelerating tube A, to obtain beams of protons, or any other charged atom projectiles, with energies of several crocodiles.

Much more ingenious is the atom smasher invented by E. O. Lawrence and generally known as a *cyclotron*. In contrast to the electrostatic generator, the cyclotron accelerates the charged particles by giving them a large number of successive electric kicks, using each time a comparatively low voltage. This eliminates the use of very high potentials, which are a necessary attribute of the electrostatic-generator, and makes the cyclotron a much more compact and convenient apparatus to work with. The principle of the cyclotron lies in a well-known physical fact that a charged particle moving through a homogeneous magnetic field is deflected from its original direction of motion, and, instead of moving along a straight line, describes a circle. The radius of the circle depends on the strength of the magnetic field as well as on the velocity of the particle: the faster the particle is moving, the smaller the deflection and, consequently, the larger the circle. The point which made the construction of the cyclotron possible lies in the fact that the radius and consequently the total length of the circular trajectory is proportional to the velocity of the particle. From this it follows that the time necessary for the particle to go once around will be the same for slow as for fast particles, since each increase of a particle's velocity will lead to a corresponding increase of the length of the circular trajectory

along which it must move. Remembering this, it is now
easy to understand the work of the cyclotron which is
presented schematically in Fig. 16. It consists of a circular

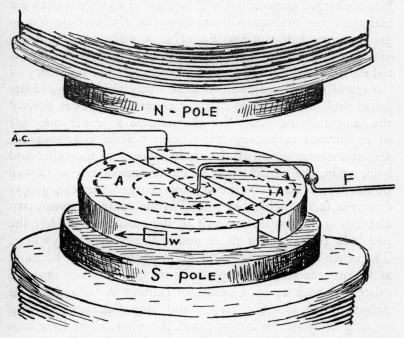

Fig. 16. The scheme of Lawrence's cyclotron. The upper pole of the
electromagnet is moved up to show the accelerator-box, and the upper part
of that box assumed to be transparent. F is the tube feeding the charged
projectiles (ions of the material to be used for bombardment, W is the
window through which ions are escaping, A.C. is the connection to the
high tension alternating current.

metallic box cut into two halves A and A¹, and placed between the poles of a large electromagnet producing a uniform
magnetic field. The two half-boxes are connected with a
transformer producing an alternating electric tension of a
certain frequency. Thus these two half boxes will be alter-

nately charged + —; — +; + —; and so on. When a
charged particle is moving within one of the half-boxes it is
not acted upon by any electric field (since the entire half-
box is charged uniformly), and will go in a circle due to the
action of the magnet. When, however, the particle has to
go from one half-box into the other it will be either accelerated or slowed down, depending on the sign of the potential the other half-box has at this moment. If the frenquency of
the transformer is adjusted in such a way that the two half-
boxes exchange the signs of their electric charges at exactly
the same time necessary for the particle to cover one half
of its circular trajectory, the motion will be synchronized,
and at each transition from one half-box into the other and
back again, the particle will be either accelerated or slowed
down. If we send a beam of slow-charged particles (ions)
from the feeding-chamber placed in the center between two
alternating half-boxes, one half of the particles will have the
bad luck to be out of phase and will never get anywhere.
The other half, however, will be in phase and will be more
and more accelerated by going from one half-box into the
other and back again. Constantly gaining in velocity, these
particles will describe larger and larger semicircles thus
moving along an unwinding spiral. But since, as we have seen
above, the period of rotation does not depend on the velocity
of the particle, they will always remain in phase with the
oscillating electric field. Finally, when the radius of the unwinding spiral-trajectory becomes comparable with the radius
of the circular box, the beam of particles is let out through
a little window in its wall. The maximum energy to which
atomic projectiles can be accelerated in such a device depends
on the size and power of the electromagnet used to bend
the trajectories into the spiral. The two largest cyclotrons
now in use (in the University of California and in the
Carnegie Institution in Washington, D. C.) have the poles

of the magnet 60 inches across and can produce proton beams with energies up to 25 crocodiles. A still larger 184-inch cyclotron is now being installed in California which will be able to produce atomic projectiles up to 100 crocodiles.

By using accelerating devices of the above described types, physicists were able to produce fast beams of charged atomic projectiles with the intensities of 10^{15} particles per second. But one must not be too much impressed by this number of atomic projectiles since each of them is just one atom. In fact, 10^{15} projectiles per second means only $10^{+15} \times 1.66 \times 10^{-24}$ or about 10^{-9} gram per second, so that in order to turn one gram of material into a beam of atomic projectiles, the cyclotron must be run for a period of about thirty years!

But the main disadvantage of atomic projectiles obtained by means of different electric accelerators, lies not so much in the small intensities of the beams produced, as in the small effectiveness of the charged projectiles in producing nuclear transformations in the target material. The point is that the nuclei forming the cores of various atoms are always surrounded by electronic envelopes which have the property of slowing down charged projectiles moving through them. Since the target area of each atomic envelope is much larger than the target area of the nucleus, and since one cannot, of course, aim the atomic projectiles directly at the nucleus, each such projectile will have to pierce many atomic envelopes before it will have a chance of delivering a direct blow to one of the nuclei. The situation is explained graphically in Fig. 17 where atomic nuclei are represented by solid black spheres and their electronic envelopes by the lighter shadows. The ratio of the nuclear diameters to the diameters of the surrounding electronic envelopes are strongly exaggerated in that figure for purely graphical reasons. We know in fact that atomic radii are about 10^{-8} centimeters, whereas the radii of atomic nuclei are somewhat less than 10^{-12} cm, i.e., ten

thousand times smaller. This makes the target area of the
nucleus some hundred million times smaller than the target
area of the surrounding envelope, giving to the stray projectile which enters the atom only one chance in hundred
millions to hit the nucleus. On the other hand when the
charged projectile passes through the diffused atomic envelopes it loses some of its original energy due to electric
interaction with electrons forming these envelopes, and is
thus gradually slowed down and put out of action. The
ordinary charged projectiles, like protons or alpha-particles,
used in the experiments on atomic bombardment are known
to lose practically their entire energy after piercing a few

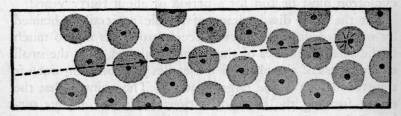

Fig. 17.

hundred thousand soft atomic bodies. This seems quite a lot,
but since, as we remember, the chance of hitting the nucleus
is about one in several hundred millions, there will be only
one projectile in several thousands which will collide with
the nucleus before it is hopelessly slowed down. Thus, even
if each direct hit at the nucleus results in its breaking down,
which is not necessarily true, most of the projectiles will be
lost, and only very few will do their job. It is clear that,
under such circumstances, there can be no mention of any
energy-profit, since although the "lucky-hits" may double
or triple the energy of the projectile, the energy of the
thousands of other projectiles will be hopelessly lost. *Thus,
although the process of atomic bombardment by artificially*

PLATE II.

The first picture of the artificial transformation of an atomic nucleus, taken by P. M. S. Blackett in Cambridge. One of the alpha-particles of the beam hits the nucleus of a nitrogen atom in the air. The long thin track extending to the left represents the passage of a proton kicked out of the nucleus. The short track belongs to the recoil nucleus. ($_7N^{14} + {}_2He^4 \rightarrow {}_8O^{17} + {}_1H^1$).

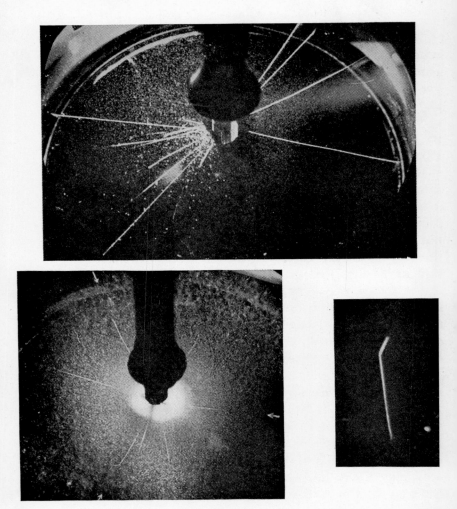

PLATE III.

Transformations of atomic nuclei caused by artificially accelerated projectiles photographed by Drs. Dee and Feather in Cambridge. *a*. A fast deuteron hits another deuteron from the heavy hydrogen gas in the chamber, producing the nuclei of tritium and ordinary hydrogen $(_1D^2 + _1D^2 \rightarrow _1T^3 + _1H^1)$. *b*. A fast proton hits the nucleus of boron, breaking it into three equal parts $(_5B^{11} + _1H^1 = 3 \, _2He^4)$. *c*. A neutron coming from the left and invisible in the picture breaks the nucleus of nitrogen into a nucleus of boron (upward track) and a nucleus of helium (downward track). $(_7N^{14} + _0n^1 \rightarrow _5B^{11} + _2HE^4)$.

accelerated charged projectiles can produce a token-disinte-
gration of various nuclei, and is therefore extremely useful
for the study of processes of this kind, it does not give us
any hope of liberating atomic energy for practical purposes.

The difficulties involved in the process of atomic bombardment suggest, however, two principal ways to produce
atomic disintegrations on a large scale. What we have to do
is to prevent, somehow, the atomic projectiles from being
slowed down by atomic electrons.

One way to do it is to make the atoms and nuclei move
speedily, not by accelerating them in some electric machine,
but rather by heating a mixture of the target- and projectile-
materials to a very high temperature. If the temperature is
sufficiently high, violent collisions between these particles
due to the thermal agitation, will possess sufficient energy to
lead to the transformation of the colliding particles. Even if
the chance of the reaction taking place in each individual
collision is very small, the persistence of such collisions will
finally have that effect since the thermal motion never stops.
This method requires, however, a temperature of hundreds
of thousands or even millions of degrees.

Another way of escaping the slowing-down effect of
atomic envelopes is to use neutral projectiles, i.e. neutrons,
which scarcely interact at all with electrons, and will move
through the material of the target at their original high speed
until they finally meet a nucleus. Since, however, free neutrons do not exist in nature and each time have to be kicked
out of the nuclei by the highly unproductive method of
proton—or alpha-particle—bombardment, their use can be
justified only if one can devise a method by which these
ideal atomic projectiles can be produced in large quantities.
Such a method has been found in the *neutron-multiplication-
process,* the possibility of which is entirely due to some
peculiar properties of a certain rare isotope of uranium.

In the following chapters we shall see the possibilities which lie in both methods and shall learn that, whereas our sun, and all other stars, produce their energy by the thermal method, human science prefers, at least for the present, to use the less natural method of neutron-multiplication.

II. *HOW THE STARS USE ATOMIC ENERGY*

1. *Alchemical burning.*

At the end of the previous chapter we came to the conclusion that the natural way of producing alchemical reactions consists in heating the substances in question to such high temperatures that the violent thermal collisions between the particles are sufficient to cause their transformations. This is, of course, the exact method customarily followed by chemists who use heat to start or to accelerate ordinary chemical transformations. We must remember, however, that it takes much more energy to break an atom than to break a molecule, so that the temperatures necessary for inducing alchemic transformations must be correspondingly higher. In fact, whereas the activation-energy of the reaction between chlorine and hydrogen, leading to the formation of hydrochloric acid ($Cl_2 + H_2 \rightarrow 2\ HCl$), is only 0.3 electron-volts, the corresponding energy of the reaction between the atoms of lithium and hydrogen ($_3Li^7 + {}_1H^1 \rightarrow 2\ {}_2He^4$) is 1.3 million electron volts (or crocodiles). Similarly, whereas the metastable molecule of nitroglycerine (comp. Fig. 2, Ch. I) will break up if the energy of only 2.2 electron volts is communicated to it, the process of nuclear fission of uranium requires the two million times larger energy of 5 crocodiles.

It is not difficult to make an estimate of the temperatures which would be necessary to produce alchemic transformations. We know from elementary physics that the energy of thermal motion of the particles of any given substance is proportional to its *absolute temperature,* i.e., to the tempera-

55

ture counted from the *absolute-zero-point* ($-273\,°C$) at which all thermal motion completely ceases. In this absolute temperature-scale the normal room temperature (ca $70\,°F$) is 292 degrees,* and the temperature of a very hot day (ca $100\,°F$) being 307 degrees it is about 5 percent higher. As another example we can mention that lead melts when the absolute temperature is about twice that of the normal room value, and that in this absolute scale the surface of the sun ($6,000\,°C$) is twenty times hotter than the surface of the earth.

Since the kinetic energy of thermal motion is proportional to the absolute temperature, and since alchemic transformations require a few million times larger collision-energies than ordinary chemical transformations, we conclude that alchemical reactions would occur only at temperatures a few million times higher than those which we encounter in ordinary chemistry. From the fact that ordinary chemical reactions usually take place at an appreciable rate at temperatures of a few hundred degrees, we conclude that alchemic reactions would require in general temperatures ranging into hundreds of millions of degrees. However the phenomenon of quantum-leakage discussed in Section 7 facilitates the process of thermonuclear reactions and causes them to go at an appreciable rate even at temperature of a few million degrees.

A glance at Fig. 14 of the previous chapter, representing activation energies of various nuclear transformations, shows us that the exact value of the alchemical reaction temperature must depend essentially on the kind of atoms involved. Since these activation-energies have the smallest values near the beginning and near the end of the periodic system of elements, we conclude that *the most promising thermonuclear*

---

* To translate Fahrenheit-scale into Centigrade-scale we have to subtract 32 from Fahrenheit value and multiply the result by 5/9. To get the absolute temperature add 273 to Centigrade-value.

reactions are those of "thermofusion" of the lightest elements, and "thermo-fission" of the heavier ones.

In discussing the rates of thermonuclear reactions, and the temperatures which are necessary for their initiation, it is essential to take into account two important factors which considerably facilitate processes of that kind.

The first factor lies in the statistical distribution of the velocities, which results from the irregularity of thermal collisions between particles. In fact, one must not think that all the particles of a given substance at a certain temperature will move at exactly the same speed: some of them may be slowed down by adverse collisions, others can receive, in similar cases, abnormally high velocities. Thus, whereas for any given temperature of a substance we shall always have a well-defined *mean-velocity* of its particles, there will always be present a certain percentage with abnormally slow and abnormally high velocities.

The distribution-law of thermal velocities is studied in the branch of science known as statistical physics, and is expressed by a formula first derived by the British scientist *Clerk Maxwell*. This Maxwell distribution law is shown graphically in Fig. 18, where the relative number of particles possessing a given kinetic energy of motion is plotted against the value of this kinetic energy. We see that, although for any given temperature, some particles are always present with energies much higher than the average value, their number decreases very rapidly with the increasing energy excess.

It is easy to see how this statistical distribution of energies affects the rates of both molecular and atomic reactions. In fact, if every particle of a substance had exactly the mean energy corresponding to the given temperature, no reaction at all would take place at temperatures for which this mean energy is lower than the activation-energy of the transformation involved. On the contrary, for temperatures just above that critical value every single collision between two particles would lead to their transformation, and the reaction would result in an instantaneous explosion. We know very well that this is not the case, and that the rates of all ordinary chemical reactions increase gradually with the increasing temperature.

The fact that thermal reactions occur at temperatures which are well below the critical activation-value, and are

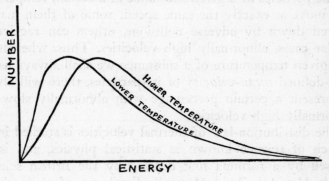

Fig. 18.

only slowly accelerated when the temperature rises, is due to the presence of abnormally fast particles which are able to produce some transformations, even though the mean energy is not high enough. Since the number of such fast particles (given by what is known as the "tail" of Maxwell's distribution-curve), is small, the reaction takes place with corresponding slowness. With the increase of temperature of a substance, the number of particles able to produce transformation increases rapidly (since the maximum of the curve in Fig. 19 moves to the right), thus causing the increased rate of reaction.

It may be noticed here that all chemical reactions observed

under laboratory conditions, including such speedy reactions as those taking place in the processes of explosion, are due to the action of such extra-fast particles in the statistical

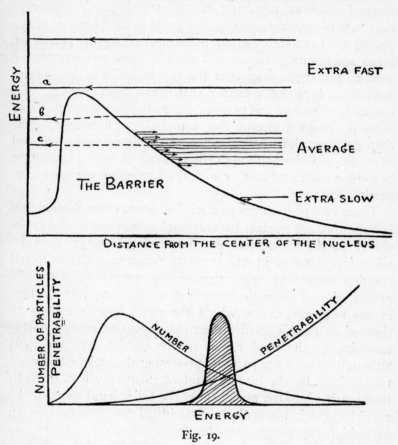

Fig. 19.

distribution. The kinetic energy of 2.2 electron-volts, for example, which corresponds to the activation energy of a nitroglycerine-molecule, will be reached by the plurality of nitroglycerine molecules only at the temperature of 25,000°C, whereas we know very well that nitroglycerine will decompose and explode at much lower initial temperatures.

The second factor, which is of particular importance in the thermal reactions involving atomic nuclei, lies in the phenomenon of quantum-leakage discussed in the previous chapter. As we have seen there, a particle climbing the barrier of force surrounding an atomic nucleus does not necessarily need to go all the way over the top in order to get inside, since there is always a chance that it can "leak through" the barrier by virtue of this peculiar quantum phenomenon. Thus, there is always a chance that a particle with energy lower than the activation-energy will penetrate into the nucleus and cause the reaction, although the chances of such penetration become smaller and smaller with the decreasing energy of the particle.*

These two phenomena of statistical energy distribution and leakage through nuclear barriers both contribute to the probability of thermo-nuclear reaction and necessarily must be taken into account in any accurate estimate of the expected reaction rates. The upper part of Fig. 19 gives a schematic presentation of the main features of a thermonuclear reaction at the temperature for which the mean kinetic energy of thermal motion is smaller than the activation-energy corresponding to the total height of the barrier. We see that, although most of the particles possessing the mean energy are turned back by the barrier, some of them may leak through thus getting into the nucleus. On the other hand some of the particles which, because of the statistical distribution, have an extra-high energy get into the nucleus directly over the top of the barrier. There is also an intermediate case where a particle which has only a comparatively small energy-excess

---

* A similar phenomenon of "leaking through" can be also expected in ordinary chemical reactions between molecules, but calculations have shown that its importance in this case is very small.

over the mean-value gets into the nucleus by the process of leaking through the barrier. Since the penetrability of the barrier increases with the increasing energy-excess of the incident particles, whereas the number of such particles rapidly decreases, it is apparent that there must be some optimum energy excess for which the effect will be at its maximum.

This is illustrated by the curves given in the lower part of Fig. 19. One curve, representing the number of particles with a given energy (Maxwell-curve), drops rapidly towards the right, whereas the other curve, representing the penetrability, rapidly increases. The total number of penetrations, which is apparently given by the product of the number of particles with a given energy and the corresponding penetrability, is shown by the heavy curve. We see that the maximum effect is actually due to a particular group of particles with an excess of energy sufficiently high to result in a high penetrability, but not so high as to effect too great a reduction in the number of such particles in the statistical distribution.

The formula for the rate of various thermonuclear reactions based on the above described picture of the process was first derived, in 1929, by *R. Atkinson* and *F. Houtermans*, and later improved on the basis of the more modern theory of nuclear processes by *G. Gamow* and *E. Teller*. This formula, which looks rather terrifying for a person not skilled in mathematics, does not have a place in this book, and we shall give here only some results concerning the rates of nuclear reactions which can be obtained by its straightforward application.

As mentioned several times before, the highest reaction-rates must be expected in the reactions between nuclei of the lightest elements, since the repulsion between the electric charges preventing the contact of two colliding nuclei has in this case the smallest value. *The best nuclear reaction from this point of view is the reaction between two deuterons (nuclei of heavy hydrogen), since in this case each of the two colliding particles carries only one elementary electric charge.* This reaction has been studied directly by the method of atomic bombardment in experiments where a beam of deuterons, accelerated to a high speed in cyclotron, is directed on a heavy-water target. The reaction between two colliding deuterons has been found to proceed according to the equation:

$$_1D^2 + {}_1D^2 \rightarrow {}_2He^3 + {}_0n^1$$

with the formation of one nucleus of light helium-isotope, one neutron, and the liberation of 3.2 crocodiles of energy. By substituting the numerical data pertaining to this reaction, as obtained from bombardment experiments, into the theoretical formula for thermonuclear reactions, one can calculate the rates of atomic energy production which can be expected at different temperatures.

The results of such calculations are presented graphically in Fig. 20, where the rate of energy generation (in calories per second, per gram of the material used) is plotted against the absolute temperature.* We see from this figure that no appreciable liberation of atomic energy begins before the temperature rises to several hundred thousand degrees. At four hundred thousand degrees a gram of deuterium liberates 0.001 calories per second, so that we should have to wait for 100,000 seconds, or nearly a whole day, to accumulate enough energy for boiling an equal amount of water. At eight hundred thousand degrees, thermonuclear energy liberation reaches a hundred calories per second, or, in electric

---

* The values given in this figure correspond to the assumption that one uses a highly compressed deuterium gas with a density comparable to that of water. For a smaller density as, for example that of the atmospheric air, the rate of energy liberation per gram will be a thousand times smaller.

power units, about 400 watts.* It would be a nice heating-unit for a large coffee-pot.† Since, as we have seen before, the total nuclear energy contained in one gram of the material is about 2.10^{10} calories, such a heating unit would keep our coffee-pot warm continuously for 2.10^8 seconds or for about six years. If we now raise the temperature of our gram of deuterium to twelve hundred thousand degrees, the rate of

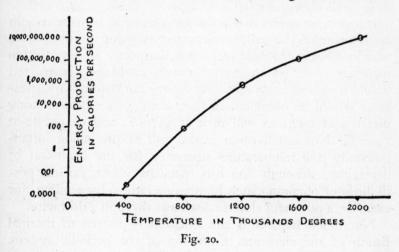

Fig. 20.

nuclear energy liberation will be one million calories per second, or in electric power units four thousand kilowatts. This is just about the power necessary to run a small factory. The energy liberation will, however, last at this rate for only 6 hours. At still higher temperatures we come dangerously close to the possibility of nuclear explosion at which all the available energy will be liberated almost instantaneously.

* One watt is 0.25 calories per second.
† We refer here to the amount of energy liberated in the nuclear reaction, and not to the heating which can be obtained from the piece of material at such high initial temperature.

Thus we see that the thermonuclear reaction in deuterium could be used as a source of power for driving all kinds of machinery if only we could succeed in building a furnace with a constant temperature of a few hundred thousand degrees; and that a small charge of deuterium could be used as an explosive with tremendous destructive power if only we could devise the means for raising its temperature instantaneously well above one million degrees.

It seems, however, that the construction of furnaces which could maintain the temperatures necessary for thermonuclear reactions lies in the field of pure fiction, since all conceivable materials from which such furnaces could be constructed would melt and evaporate long before the required temperatures would be obtained. In fact, even such a heat-resisting material as tungsten will melt at 3370°C, and evaporate at 5900°C! Not much easier is the task of producing instantaneously—the temperature necessary for the explosion of deuterium, although one can speculate about various possibilities of obtaining such high temperatures by sending, for example, a powerful electric discharge through a thin wire.

Not much happier is the situation in regard to thermal fission of the elements at the top of the periodic system, since the preliminary theoretical estimates seem to show that in this case the reaction requires not much lower temperatures. For all other elements located between the two extremities of the periodic system the activation-energies for fusion or fission, as the case may be, are considerably larger and the temperatures which are necessary to induce these reactions correspondingly higher.

From the above discussion we see that *the main difficulty standing in our way of achieving the "steady alchemic burning" of various chemical elements lies in the impossibility of constructing furnaces which would not melt and turn into gas long before the required temperatures could be reached.*

But what is impossible on the earth may well be possible
in the cosmos, and we shall see in the next section that the
stars represent just such giant furnaces, with thick gaseous
walls held together by the forces of gravity, inside which the
processes of alchemic burning are going on, continuously
producing the energy which the stars must have to support
their radiation.

2. *Atomic furnaces in stars.*

One popular book on meteorology informed its readers
that "the phenomenon of thunderstorms was known to the
ancient Greeks." It will not be much more of an understate-
ment if we say that the phenomenon of atomic energy production in the sun was observed by prehistoric man, who
bathed himself in the warm sunshine. But, of course, neither
prehistoric man nor the ancient Egyptians who worshipped
the Sun-god, nor the medieval astrologers and alchemists,
nor even the modern scientists of only half a century ago,
ever suspected that the energy of the sun comes from the
deep interior of separate atoms forming its giant body. As
a matter of fact, the very concept of the internal energy of
an atom was not existent, since the atoms were considered
as indivisible elementary particles.

Even before the discovery of atomic transformations and
the hidden energy of the atom, it became clear that our sun,
as well as all other stars in the sky, must conceal in their
interiors some kind of unknown energy-sources which are
immensely more powerful than any source of energy hitherto
known to science. It was calculated that if the sun were
using the ordinary energy of chemical transformations, being for example built of pure carbon and burning in the
surrounding atmosphere of oxygen, it would have been
turned into ashes in just a few thousand years. Even the short
span of written human history is enough to reject such an

assumption. In the middle of the last century the German physicist *Helmholtz*, and after him the British physicist *Lord Kelvin* formulated the so-called *contractive hypothesis* according to which the sun receives its continuous energy supply from a slow but steady shrinking of its giant body. The energy which can be liberated by such a contracting sun would be enough to support its radiation for the long period of about twenty million years, but even this number was not large enough to satisfy the geologists and paleontologists who require at least a billion years to explain the evolution of life on the surface of the earth.

Thus the problem of stellar energy-sources remained a deep mystery until the year 1896, when the discovery of radioactivity by *H. Becquerel* revealed the new and hitherto unsuspected sources of energy hidden inside the atom. However, although the importance of radioactivity for the understanding of stellar energy-sources was realized almost from the very beginning, it was more than thirty years later that the relation between atomic transformations and the sources of stellar radiation was definitely established. The question had had to wait for the development of better knowledge concerning the physical conditions in the interior of stars, and the properties of nuclear-reactions.

During these years considerable progress in our understanding of the physics of stellar interiors was made, mainly due to the work of the British astronomer *Sir Arthur Eddington*, and the knowledge of atomic energy was largely expanded by the epoch-making experiments of *Lord Rutherford* on the artificial transformations of elements, and the mathematical theory of these phenomena developed by the author of the present book.

These developments made it possible for the two young physicists, *R. Atkinson* from England and *F. Houtermans* from Germany to show, in 1929, that under the conditions of high temperatures and densities existing in the central regions of stars, thermonuclear reactions of light elements could be expected to occur with a sufficiently high speed to supply all the energy necessary for stellar radiation. We have already discussed the fundamental points of the *Atkinson-Houtermans* theory of thermonuclear reactions in connection with the possibility of atomic energy liberation under artificial conditions, and we must now learn some more facts concerning the physical conditions existing in the interior of our sun and other stars.

The first important point concerning stellar structures is that they represent large spheres of very hot gas. Direct measurements show that the temperature of the solar surface, which must be the coolest part of its giant body, is about 6,000°C. We know very well that at such temperature even the most heat-resistant materials as tungsten will be completely turned into a gas. As we go deeper under the surface of the sun, the temperature steadily rises and, although we cannot make any direct measurements, we can surmise that the material near the solar center is many, many times hotter. But how hot? It would seem that any attempt to estimate the exact value of the central temperature of the sun and stars must necessarily lie in the region of pure speculation. Well, it is true, speculation it is, but as in so many instances presented by modern science, the results of such speculation can be considered to be just as certain as if we ourselves dived into the stellar interior with a thermometer in our hand. The point is that, as stated before, the stars are made entirely of gases, and the knowledge of the gaseous state of matter has progressed sufficiently far to permit us to make unambiguous predictions about the behavior of gases even at the most extreme conditions which can be expected near the center of a star. Thus, starting with the directly observed temperature and gas-pressure on the surface, we can proceed, step by step, deeper into the stellar body calculating from the well-established laws of gases, new temperatures and new pressures in each layer through which we pass in our mental journey.

In carrying through such calculations, we finally come to the values of central temperature and pressure which in the case of the sun turn out to be *20 million degrees centigrade*, and *160 billion atmospheres*. Although not obtained by direct measurements, these results can be considered to be just as certain as the estimates of the strength of a bridge, or the power of a hydroelectric installation made by a good engineer prior to the construction, on the basis of well-known laws of mechanics and hydrodynamics.

It is interesting to notice here that the exactness and certainty of the above quoted results is primarily due to the simplicity of gas laws governing the interior of stellar bodies. In fact we can be much more certain about the deep interior of the distant stars than about the state of solid matter forming the core of the Earth only a few hundred miles under our feet.

In making similar calculations in the case of various stars, *Eddington* came to the very interesting conclusion that, whereas the surface temperatures of stars can vary from only one or two thousand to over ten thousand degrees, and whereas their luminosities differ often by a factor of millions, their central temperatures remain always very close to the value of 20 million degrees obtained for the sun. Thus the central temperature of the giant star known as Y Cygni, which is about a thousand times brighter than the sun, is only 30 millions, whereas the very faint star Krüger 60 has in its interior a temperature of about 15 million degrees. It looks as if most of the stars maintain their interiors at about the same temperature—presumably necessary for some specific thermonuclear reaction, and vary it slightly to take care of the differences in their luminosities. In fact, we have seen in the previous section (on the example of deuterium reaction) that small changes of the temperature will suffice to change the rate of energy-production in a thermonuclear reaction by a very large factor.

We have to find out now which, of all possible alchemical reactions, is *the* reaction which supplies the energy to our sun and other stars large and small. In order to answer this question we have apparently to apply the *Atkinson-Houtermans* formula for the rate of alchemic reactions to various possible alchemic transformations, and to see which of them has the appropriate rate of energy-liberation at temperatures of about 20 million degrees.

We can say, first of all, that this *stellar reaction* is certainly not the thermonuclear reaction in deuterium discussed in the previous section. In fact we have seen that this reaction goes at full rate at temperatures of only a few hundred thousand degrees consuming all the material in just six hours at only three hundred thousand degrees. If there were some deuterium in the hot solar interior it would certainly be consumed in a negligible fraction of a second, and thus could not have been responsible for the long life of the sun. In Table I we give a list of various alchemical reactions between the light elements which could be considered as candidates for the honorable place of stellar, energy-producing reactions. For each of these reactions we give the time which is necessary for the reaction to run halfway under the conditions existing in stellar interiors.*

In looking through the numbers given in Table I we notice at once that the alchemic reactions between lithium, beryllium and boron on one side and hydrogen on the other are excluded for exactly the same reason as the deuterium-reac-

---

* These data are based on most recent calculations by H. Bethe using the improved Gamow-Teller formula.

TABLE I

The mean reaction times for various alchemical transformations under the conditions of the interior of the Sun. (Temp: 20,000,000° C, density 100 in respect to water.)

Alchemic reaction	Mean reaction time
$_3Li^7 + _1H^1 \rightarrow _2{_2}He^4$	1 min.
$_4Be^9 + _1H^1 \rightarrow _3Li^6 + _2He^4$	15 min.
$_5B^{11} + _1H^1 \rightarrow _3{_2}He^4$	3 days
$_6C^{12} + _1H^1 \rightarrow _7N^{13}$	$2.5.10^6$ years
$_7N^{14} + _1H^1 \rightarrow _8O^{15}$	5.10^7 years
$_8O^{16} + _1H^1 \rightarrow _9F^{17}$	10^{12} years
$_{17}Cl^{37} + _1H^1 \rightarrow _{18}A^{38}$	2.10^{25} years
$_2He^4 + _2He^4 \rightarrow _4Be^8$	1.10^{15} years
$_3Li^7 + _2He^4 \rightarrow _5B^{11}$	3.10^{13} years
$_6C^{12} + _2He^4 \rightarrow _8O^{16}$	2.10^{33} years

tion. They all would go *too fast*, and thus could not be responsible for the steady alchemical burning which supports the radiation of sun and stars. In fact, if there had been some of these light elements in the stellar interiors in the beginning of their evolutionary career, they would have been completely destroyed in the very first days of their life in a violent explosion.

On the other hand, such reactions as oxygen-hydrogen, chlorine-hydrogen, or the transformations involving helium (listed in the lower part of the table) are *too slow* and would not be able to supply the energy at the rate necessary for supporting the radiation of the sun and stars.

Thus we see that *the only alchemic transformations which can be made responsible for the stellar energy production are the reactions between carbon or nitrogen on one side and hydrogen on the other.*

Although the work of *Atkinson* and *Houtermans* proved definitely that the energy-production in the sun and other stars is due to thermonuclear reactions between light elements taking place in their hot interiors, the exact nature of that reaction was discovered only ten years later by the independent research of *H. Bethe* in America and *C. v. Weizsäcker* in Germany. The main point of their discovery lies in the fact that the nuclei of carbon and nitrogen which enter into an alchemic reaction with hydrogen do not vanish, but are regenerated again through a very peculiar process known as the *carbon-nitrogen-cycle*. In order to understand this process, we have to follow carefully the fate of the atoms of these two elements in the series of alchemic transformations taking place in the stellar interior. When an atom of carbon fuses with a hydrogen atom according to the equation given in the table, we get as the result an atom of nitrogen-isotope with the atomic weight 13. This process can be directly observed in a laboratory, by subjecting a carbon-target to atomic bombardment by a beam of fast protons. Experiments show that the nucleus of nitrogen 13, formed as the result of proton-capture, is an unstable nucleus and, by emitting a positive electron, transforms itself into a nucleus of the stable but rare carbon-isotope: $_6C^{13}$. The mean time necessary for such a transformation is about ten minutes. Thus the capture of protons by the ordinary carbon nucleus in the stellar interior leads to the formation of the heavier carbon isotope, the nuclei of which will hang around until they are hit again by another proton. The capture of that proton, increasing both the weight and the charge of the nucleus by one unit, will turn it into a nucleus of ordinary nitrogen with the atomic weight 14. Still another proton comes in after a while and, being captured by nitrogen 14 nucleus, turns it over into the nucleus of oxygen 15. Here, as in the first case, the nucleus formed in the reaction is unstable and within two minutes turns into a stable nucleus of nitrogen 15 through the emission of another positive electron. The nuclei of nitrogen 15, being stable, move around through the interior of the star until they are hit again by a new proton.

Here a very interesting thing, also directly observed in

laboratory experiments, takes place. If the fourth proton were captured by the nitrogen 15 nucleus as its three predecessors were, the result would be the nucleus of oxygen 16, i.e. the ordinary oxygen. But the energy liberated in the capture of that proton sets the compound nucleus of oxygen 16 in such a state of strong agitation,* that it immediately breaks up into two unequal parts. The smaller part is an alpha-particle, whereas the larger one represents the nucleus of ordinary carbon with which the entire process started.

Summarizing this somewhat lengthy description, we can say that *four protons, captured successively by a carbon nucleus (with two of the protons turning immediately into neutrons), are re-emitted again at the end of the cycle in the combined form of an alpha-particle.* The carbon-nucleus itself comes out of the reaction unchanged, like the Phoenix from the ashes, and its role consists only in helping, or *catalyzing,* as a chemist would say, the transformation of hydrogen into helium. The point is that, in order to unite into a helium nucleus without the help of a catalyzing agent, all four protons would have to meet together at some point of space, and it is easy to see that in the disorderly thermal motion the probability of such quadruple collision is incredibly small. The catalyzing nucleus catches the protons one after another, keeping them inside until all four are collected, and we have here, according to a witty remark of *Atkinson* and *Houtermans,* who first contemplated such a possibility, "a nuclear pot in which helium is being cooked from pure hydrogen." The above discussed alchemic reactions constituting the carbon-nitrogen-cycle are represented in Fig. 21, from which we also notice that instead of starting the cycle

---

* The reason why the capture of the *fourth* proton results in particularly strong agitation of the nucleus lies in the fact that each four nuclear particles make a new nuclear subgroup (alpha-group), the formation of which inside the nucleus is connected with the liberation of considerable energy which set the entire nucleus into the state of strong vibrations.

with a carbon-nucleus, we can just as well start it with a nucleus of nitrogen, or for that matter with any stable nucleus participating in the cycle. Since, in the final count,

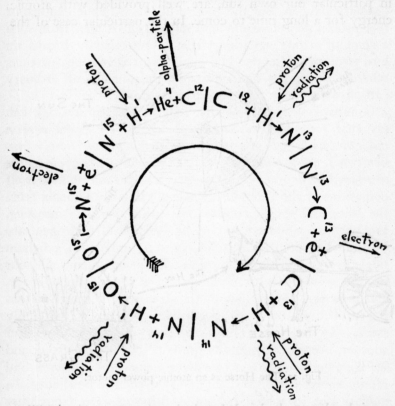

Fig. 21. "Stellar reaction." Carbon-nitrogen-cycle according to Bethe and Weizsäcker.

the stellar reaction reduces to the transformation of hydrogen into helium, the catalyzing nuclei of carbon and nitrogen remaining intact, it will last as long as there is any hydrogen left in the star.

We know from the data of astrophysics that hydrogen is the most abundant element in the Universe, forming about one-third of stellar matter. Thus the stars of the Universe, and in particular our own sun, are well provided with atomic energy for a long time to come. In the particular case of the

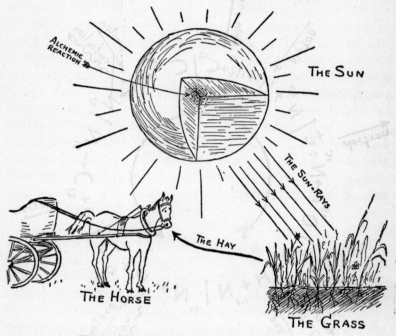

Fig. 22. The Horse as an atomic power motor.

sun, it has been calculated that during the two or three billion years of its existence it has used up only a few per cent of its original supply of alchemic fuel, and that it can still "keep going strong" for at least another ten billion years.

We see from the discussion in this section that the stellar universe is run exclusively on atomic energy sources, the radiation of all stars and in particular of our sun being supported by a steady alchemic burning taking place in their hot interiors. We can also say that all power sources used by humanity, be it the wind, water-power, coal or oil, come, in the final count, from alchemic energy-sources of the universe since they all are more or less immediate results of solar radiation. Even an old horse pulling a milk-wagon runs on atomic energy, since it is fed by hay which grew under the rays of the sun (Fig. 22). But, by using atomic energy given to us by the sun, we shall probably never be able to produce it ourselves by the same natural method of thermonuclear transformation of common elements. And it is the fortune, or maybe misfortune, of man that there is left from the great epoch of the creation of the Universe a brand of atomic nuclei known as uranium-235, the peculiar properties of which permit us to get at least one drop from the immense atomic-energy reservoirs of the Universe. But that will be the subject of the third chapter of this book.

3. *The origin of atomic fuel.*

In discussing the general problem of nuclear stability we came to the very remarkable conclusion that the world of atomic nuclei is practically saturated with hidden energy. In fact about one half of all known elements, i.e., those lighter than silver, would release their energy in the process of mutual fusion, whereas the other half, containing all heavier elements, release their energy in the breaking-up or the fission process. We have also seen that the fact that various chemical elements remain in this metastable state and do not turn into silver by a series of rapid nuclear transformations is explained by extremely high activation-energies of alchemic reactions. Even in the hottest spots of the Universe, in the deep interior of stars, the temperatures are only just high enough to produce a slow "burning" of the lightest and, from an alchemical point of view, the most "inflammable" elements. However, even these stellar furnaces are not hot enough to cause any appreciable thermonuclear transformation of the main bulk of chemical elements of the period system. Thus, apart from the slow but steady transformation of hydrogen into helium due to stellar reaction, the chemical constitution of the universe remains at present practically unchanged.

This brings us to the immediate conclusion that the Universe, as we know it now, must be only one of the later stages in the process of gradual evolution, and that a long, long time ago there must have been an epoch when our Universe was subject to entirely different physical conditions. In this distant past the materials forming different parts of the Universe apparently must have been subjected to such terrific temperatures and pressures that thermonuclear reactions involving every single element of the periodic system were occurring as easily as ordinary molecular reactions in the kettles of a chemical plant. The present relative proportions of various brands of atoms, the rarity of gold and platinum and the abundance of iron and silicon, must represent direct consequences of the situation existing at this distant epoch, and the fact that the collection of atoms forming the present Universe represents a highly metastable mixture must be connected in some way with the occurrences which took place during the long process of their formation.

Granting that such an epoch of universal "atom-cooking" must have existed once upon a time, we can ask ourselves whether we have any means to estimate that time more exactly. The only way to estimate a date of some long-past event is to look for some remnants of it which have come down to our time. But the remnants of the past which do not normally change with time are not of much help. If you see in a museum a sword which was used in the Civil War, it does not tell you whether the said war occurred fifty, one hundred, or five hundred years ago. But if you see a veteran of that war in his nice blue uniform and medals walking down the street leaning on a stick, you can be pretty sure that the war took place less than a century ago. An even better estimate can be given if you know the proportion of veterans still alive. Using the membership-list of the American Legion along with the mortality tables obtained from a life insurance company, you can probably estimate the date of the first world war with no larger error than that of a year.

Since the great event of the creation of the Universe took place at a time when there were no historians to record the date, the study of the remnants of that epoch represents our only way to place it in the scale of time. In this case the remnants are, of course, not swords and soldiers, but are atoms of the different elements which were made during this epoch. We cannot learn much from the atoms of the stable elements, since they could have been in existence from the beginning of time. But the unstable radioactive atoms which gradually decay and finally go out of existence are as good for the estimate of the age of the Universe as veterans for the estimate of the dates of wars. In fact, since, as we have seen above, no new elements can be formed now in any place of the Universe, the number of radioactive elements still remaining must give us a close check on the date of their origin. There are three known families of radioactive elements: *thorium-*, *uranium-* and *actinium-family*. Each radioactive family represents a genealogical line in which junior members are produced by the spontaneous decay of their immediate seniors. Thus the length of existence of the radioactive family depends entirely on the life-span of its senior member, and as soon as this "head of the family" completely decays nothing is left of its entire family. The average life of the three known family heads: the *thorium*, the *uranium I*, and the *actino-uranium* are known to be respectively eighteen billion, four and half billion, and four hundred million years.

It must be remembered in this connection that the decay of radioactive elements, just as the death-rate of human beings, is subjected to statistical laws, some individuals succumbing before their time, others living much longer. The life-spans given above represent only the average life periods of radioactive atoms, and we can expect small fractions of them to survive for a much longer time.

We know that in the present epoch thorium and uranium I are only slightly less abundant in nature than other heavy stable elements as for example lead,* which means that they have not yet had enough time to decay since their formation. On the other hand, the considerably shorter-lived actino-uranium (which is known as U-235 and which, as we shall see later, is used as the charge of the atomic bomb) is much less abundant, representing only 0.7 per cent of ordinary uranium, from which we can conclude that the main bulk of that particular brand of atoms has already decayed, and that only a small fraction of particularly long-lived "individuals" is still left. Remembering the above given life-spans of the three radioactive-family-heads, *we can fix the time of their origin as being about three billion years ago.*

This number is in remarkable accord with various other data about the age of the Universe. Thus, for example, from the rate of hydrogen-consumption in the alchemic reaction supplying the stars with their energy *we can conclude that the expected life-span of an average star must run into billions of years.*

The data about stellar motion in general, and the behavior of the so-called double stars in particular, indicate that *the society of stars forming our system of the Milky Way cannot*

---

* The relative abundance of lead, thorium and uranium in the earth-crust are expressed by numbers 10:8:2.

be much older than a few billion years. Finally, the data of geology *suggest a few billion years as the age of our Earth, which, according to the modern cosmogonical theories, must have originated from primordial chaos about the same time as the sun and other stars.*

But the most interesting fact, which also gives us a definite picture of what was happening in this distant past when the face of the Universe was first shaping up, lies in the phenomenon of Universal expansion, discovered by the Mt. Wilson astronomer *E. Hubble* about twenty years ago.

It has been known for quite some time that our sun represents just one insignificant member of a giant stellar system known as the system of the Milky Way or the Galaxy. It was also known that our Galaxy, which contains about forty billion separate stars, is not a single stellar island in the unlimited vastnesses of empty space, but that, on the contrary, there are innumerable other galaxies, very similar to our own, scattered more or less uniformly through space as far as can be seen through the most powerful telescope.

In studying the motion of these distant stellar systems, *Hubble* discovered that they are in a state of general recession from each other and from our Galaxy, flying apart as the fragments resulting from some giant explosion. By measuring the speed of the galactic recession it is not difficult to calculate the date when it started, and when all material of the Universe, which is now loosely scattered through the space, was packed much closer together. *The date of this original super-dense state of the Universe comes out to be two or three billion years ago,* which is about the same date as we had before for the origin of radioactive elements, the origin of stars, and, as a small personal point, for the origin of our own Earth.

We can now visualize the entire picture of the evolution of the Universe, as beginning with the state of extremely dense and hot primordial gas, the "original chaos," which was rapidly expanding in what could be termed a giant explosion under the action of its terrifically high pressure. As the result of this rapid expansion the originally uniform gas must have been broken up into a large number of small gaseous spheres, which we now call the stars, which in their turn formed the separate stellar clouds or galaxies rapidly driven apart by the momentum of the primary explosion.

Not entering into various astronomical consequences which follow from this breath-taking picture of the creation of our Universe, we shall here be mostly interested in the fact that it leads exactly to the conditions of extremely high temperatures and pressures which we found to be necessary for the formation of chemical elements. Indeed, during the sufficiently early stages of expansion, the gas forming that primordial chaos must have been as dense and as hot as one could desire, and the transformations of one chemical element into another must have been going on with the greatest ease. Thus, this must have been the time when the present proportions of the various stable chemical elements were first laid down, and when a large number of unstable elements, some of which have survived to the present time, was formed. In particular, the formation of actino-uranium which, as we shall see in the next chapter, is the element which gave us the possibility of at least partial utilization of atomic energy, dates back to the early days of the Universe.

If we ask ourselves about the details of the process which was responsible for the present abundance of various elements, two different possibilities immediately present themselves. The elements could have originated as the result of some alchemical equilibrium corresponding to high temperatures and pressures prevailing during the early days of the Universe, or they could have been formed in an irregular breaking up process connected with the rapid expansion.

The first possibility, that of alchemic equilibrium at very high temperatures, was investigated by several authors, particularly by *Henrich* and *Chandrasekhar*. According to that point of view, the nuclei of various elements violently reacting with each other as the result of very high temperature, probably several billion degrees, must have finally come to a certain state of equilibrium in which their relative proportions were not changing any more, being completely determined by the existing temperature and pressure. The situation is exactly similar to that of an ordinary chemical equilibrium between the molecules of various chemical compounds. Thus, for example, if we bring water vapor to higher and higher temperatures the molecules of water will begin to break up, or as we say *dissociate*, under the violence of thermal collisions. For each temperature and pressure there will be certain proportions of original (non-dissociated) water molecules mixed with hydrogen and oxygen atoms from the broken-up molecules. We say that for each particular temperature and pressure there exists a certain chemical equilibrium between the original substance and its dissociation products. At a very high temperature of, say, five thousand degrees, thermal dissociation will be complete and no unbroken water-molecules will be left. If now the temperature begins to decrease slowly, the atoms of hydrogen and oxygen, colliding less vigorously, will begin to stick together again forming molecules of water. Coming down to $100°$ C we find in the vessel the same watervapor with which we started. This so-called reversible dissociation-reaction is usually expressed by the chemical formula:

$$H_2O \rightleftarrows 2H + O$$

We will encounter, however, an entirely different situation if the cooling of the dissociated water-vapor is accompished very rapidly by sending it, for example, through liquid air.

In such rapid cooling, the oxygen- and hydrogen-gas forming the product of dissociation will not have time to reunite again into water, and, although some amount of water will undoubtedly be formed, there will also be some unreacted hydrogen and oxygen left over. Since, at lower temperatures, the reaction between these two gases goes very slowly, they will represent a metastable mixture with hidden chemical energy. Put in a lighted match, an explosion will occur as the result of which the mixture of gases turns back into original water vapor.

According to the equilibrium theory of the origin of chemical elements, their present metastability is due to exactly the same reasons as in the above example. Under the influence of extremely high temperatures and pressures corresponding to the "pre-stellar" stage of the Universe, numerous dissociations and associations between various nuclei were taking place, leading to a certain alchemical equilibrium with the well-defined relative proportions of different brands of atoms. As the result of the subsequent rapid expansion of the primordial gas, and the resulting rapid drop of its temperature, this distribution must have been "frozen up" in the very same way as the dissociation products of the water vapor. If the relative percentages of different elements correspond to the state of alchemical equilibrium at certain very high temperature and pressure, we should be able to calculate what these temperatures and pressures must have been in order to lead to the observed abundances of chemical elements in nature. To do this one can use an ordinary formula for chemical equilibrium taken from any textbook of physical chemistry, dressing it, however, in an alchemical mantle. Calculations of such a kind were carried out in great detail by *Henrich* and *Chandrasekhar* with partially very encouraging results. They were able to show that the present proportions of the elements in the first half of the periodic system, up to the smallest details, can be explained as the result of alchemical equilibrium at the temperature of 8 billion degrees, the pressure of 7.10^{18} atmospheres, and the density of ten million water density. These are physical conditions which easily could have been present in the early stages of universal expansion.

But, and it is a very important "but," the theory of alchemical equilibrium fails hopelessly in the case of heavier elements. A glance at Fig. 23, in which the continuous curve represents the observed relative abundances of different elements in nature, explains the situation. We see that beginning with the most abundant element, hydrogen,* the relative proportions of elements decrease rapidly with the increasing atomic weight. But, beyond silver the curve straightens out, showing about equal abundances of all elements in the second half of the periodic system. This is exactly the point which the theory of alchemic equilibrium is unable to explain, since the theoretical curve, shown in Fig. 23, by a broken line, would continue to descend thus predicting for such heavy elements as gold, lead or radioactive elements abundances hundreds of millions times smaller than those which have been observed.

One can try to avoid this difficulty by saying that perhaps the reactions involving the heavier elements have been "frozen" before those involving the light ones, since the transformations of heavy elements require in general much higher temperatures. Thus the present abundances of the elements in the second part of the periodic system may still correspond to equilibrium, but equilibrium at still much

---

* As we have already mentioned, hydrogen forms 35 per cent of stellar material, and according to most recent astrophysical views may be even as much as 99 per cent. A comparatively small abundance of hydrogen on the Earth is due to a specific condition which permitted the main bulk of original hydrogen-content of our planet to escape from its atmosphere into interstellar space.

higher temperatures and pressures than the above quoted values for lighter elements. Such a hypothesis would, however, not withstand the fact that heavier elements are subject

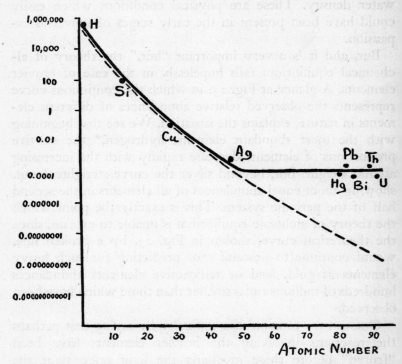

Fig. 23. Relative abundances of various chemical elements in nature plotted against their atomic numbers. Only a few individual elements are shown in the diagram, but all others fall with small deviations on the same continuous curve. The broken line represents the abundances expected on the basis of the theory of alchemic equilibrium.

to immediate fission in the collisions with free neutrons. Indeed, even if the heavy elements were formed at an earlier stage of expansion, and by the time when the temperature of matter dropped to eight billion degrees would not be subject to ordinary thermonuclear reactions,* they could still be broken up by the collisions with neutrons. And there must have been plenty of rather fast free neutrons around when the large-scale transformation of lighter elements was going on!

If the present proportions of elements cannot be due to the slow equilibrium processes in the steadily expanding material, the only possibility left is to assume an almost instantaneous expansion, of an explosive nature, in which various atomic nuclei were formed in a way similar to fragments from a bursting shell. To do this we have to start with a still earlier stage of expansion when the material of the Universe was squeezed to a density of 10^{14} grams per cubic centimeter which, as we have seen above, represents the density of nuclear fluid. At this stage, not only were the stars non-existent, but there were also no separate atoms, space being filled up with the continuous super-dense fluid under terrific pressure. The matter which now fills the visible part of the Universe (i.e. up to a distance of about 500 million light years † as seen through the Mt. Wilson telescope) was squeezed into a sphere with a radius of only about three million miles, i.e., ten times the radius of the orbit of the moon! And the parts of the Universe which are now too far away to be seen even through the most powerful telescope, formed parts of the nuclear fluid beyond this distance.

As the result of the rapid explosive expansion, that primordial fluid must have been broken into separate drops, each drop being miles, or maybe hundreds or millions of miles, across. But, as we have seen in the first chapter, large drops

---

* As remarked in the first section of the present chapter, the thermonuclear reaction of fission in the heaviest elements may not require much higher temperatures than the ordinary thermonuclear reactions between lighter elements.

† A light-year, i.e., the distance covered by light in the course of one year, is equal to 9,460,000,000,000 kilometers.

of nuclear fluid are unstable unless their radius becomes smaller than 0.00000000001 cm. which is the radius of a heavy atomic nucleus. The big drops of nuclear fluid formed in the very first moments of expansion, must have been continuously

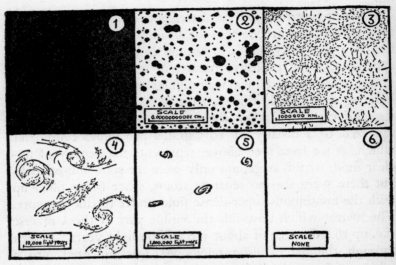

Fig. 24. Pictorial history of the Universe. 1. All space is filled continuously by super-dense nuclear fluid. 2. Nuclear fluid breaks up into separate drops and a series of successive fission-processes lead to the formation of nuclei of different elements. 3. The original gas breaks up into separate giant spheres: the stars. If this drawing were done correctly there would be about 10^{57} separate points (atoms) in each group. 4. The originally uniform distribution of stars breaks up into giant stellar systems: the galaxies. In a correct drawing there should be about 40 billion stars per galaxy. 5. Galaxies are drawn apart by universal expansion. 6. Everything is so expanded that you can see nothing at all.

breaking into smaller and still smaller parts until they finally came down to the normal size of atomic nuclei. Here the process of further fission had stopped, due to the preponderance of nuclear surface-forces over the electric forces of repulsion. *Thus the continuous nuclear fluid, which formed*

Fig. 25. A modern version of the old Arabian story about a poor fisherman and a jinni imprisoned in a bottle.

*the original universe, was pulverized into an incredibly large number of small droplets which, enveloping themselves with electronic shells * became the atoms of various chemical elements.* The above described *fission-theory of the origin of chemical elements,* fantastic as it may seem, gives us quite a satisfactory explanation of the existence in nature of the heavy, easily fissionable elements such as uranium or thorium. It also explains quite satisfactorily the observed equal abundances of the heavy elements, since, indeed, it is not difficult to show that in the process of irregular fragmentation the number of fragments of different sizes must be expected to be about the same (Fig. 24). However this non-equilibrium theory is also not entirely free from contradictions, encountering serious difficulties when called to explain the large amount of lighter elements. It must be hoped that the existing conflict between the above two points of view will soon be resolved by further investigations.

Summing up the facts and theories discussed in the present section we may say that the atomic energy hidden in the interior of the nuclei was concentrated there in the very first days of the creation of the Universe, and is therefore a much older treasure than the energy of coal which was accumulated from the sun's rays only a few million years ago. Owing to the extremely great heights of the barriers surrounding atomic nuclei, this energy sits there like the fabled jinni in the bottle, and is only slowly leaking out under the terrifically high temperatures of solar and stellar interiors, thus providing light, heat, and the beauty of the world.

But when man lets the jinni out of U-235 (Fig. 25), he had best be prepared. The jinni of atomic energy can do terrific damage if encouraged for evil!

---

* The original nuclear fluid probably consisted exclusively of neutrons, subsequent transformation of which into protons liberated negative electric charges which formed the electronic envelopes of the atoms.

III. *HOW CAN MAN USE ATOMIC ENERGY?*

1. *The advantage of neutron-bombardment.*

When the neutrons were first discovered in the year 1932, it was immediately recognized that the absence of electric charge makes them ideal projectiles for the purposes of atomic bombardment. As we have seen in the first chapter, the main disadvantage of ordinary atomic projectiles, like protons or alpha-particles, lies in their electric charge. The forces of interaction between this electric charge and the electrons which form the envelopes of the bombarded atoms, cause the charged projectiles to lose their energy very quickly in flying through the material of the target. This reduces the chances of high speed collisions between the projectiles and the target-nuclei to only one in several thousands. But even when such collisions take place, the strong repulsion between the electric charge of the projectile and that of the nucleus forms a potential barrier which makes it very difficult for the projectile to penetrate inside the nucleus. Thus, whereas using charged projectiles accelerated to the energy of several million electron volts we were able to produce at least a token-disintegration of the first dozen elements of the periodic system, any noticeable effect in such heavy elements as mercury, lead, or uranium would require the energies up to a hundred million electron volts.

Neither of these two disadvantages of charged projectiles is present in the case of neutrons which practically do not interact at all with electrons, and are also not subject to any electric repulsive forces on the approaches to even highly charged nuclei of heavy elements. Thus every single neutron of the original beam is sure to penetrate into the internal structure of the very first nucleus which it encounters on its way, with a good chance of producing a transformation. If the transformation produced by neutrons in the material of the target used liberates a certain amount of nuclear energy, we shall have energy-profit for every single neutron of the beam, in contrast to the "profit-for-one-and-total-loss-for-thousands" situation which we encountered in atomic bombardment by charged projectiles.

Thus we can easily expect a considerable net energy profit from the use of neutron-beams for atomic bombardment, provided, of course, that we can produce such beams without large expenditures of energy. But this is exactly where the difficulty lies! In fact, due to their high penetrability into atomic nuclei, free neutrons do not exist in nature, and whenever some neutrons are produced by artificial methods they will very quickly be captured and held prisoners in the atomic nuclei of the surrounding material. Thus we cannot buy a pound of "neuterium" (such might be the name of the substance made out of neutrons), and put it into some atomic accelerator. Indeed, the only way of forming a beam of neutrons consists in kicking them out of the nuclei of some other element by subjecting this element to an intensive bombardment by artificially accelerated charged projectiles. It is clear that we are here tangled in a vicious circle; in order to produce one efficient neutral projectile we must lose, without any profit, many thousands of charged ones. We shall see later in this chapter how this fundamental difficulty can be avoided by the use of a special "neutron-multiplication-process." For the present, we shall satisfy ourselves with the remark that the neutron-beams produced at a high energy cost by ordinary bombardment methods still are of great importance for the study of various transformation processes in heavy elements, due to the fact that neutron-projectiles can penetrate, without any difficulty, even into the nuclei of the heaviest element, a property which ordinary charged pro-jectiles do not possess. In fact, the study of neutron-penetra-tion into the nuclei of heavy elements led science to the discovery of the above-mentioned "multiplication-process" which finally made possible the liberation of atomic energy on a large scale.

2. Radiative capture of neutrons.

As we have seen above, a neutron which encounters an atomic nucleus on its way gets right into it as a golf-ball into a hole on the green. Being pulled inside the nuclear droplet by the cohesive forces of other neutrons and protons forming it, our neutron finds itself in the company of particles packed into the nuclear volume as tightly as sardines in a can. The kinetic energy which the neutron may have had before enter-ing into the nucleus is immediately distributed among all the particles. Even if the neutron comes along with practically no velocity the process of pulling it in will result in a wild agitation of the entire nuclear population. We remember from the general discussion of the nuclear droplet model (Ch. I Sec. 4) that to pull a neutron out of the nucleus against the cohesive forces which try to keep it in costs about 5 MeV or crocodiles in energy. It is clear that in the reverse process, when an outside neutron is pulled in, exactly as much energy will be set free inside the nucleus. (Fig. 26) As the result of this surplus internal energy, which is composed of the orig-inal kinetic energy of the neutron plus the 5 MeV produced by the cohesive forces, the entire nuclear droplet is set into a state of more or less vigorous vibration.

This phenomenon is quite similar to the pulsations which can be observed in an ordinary mercury- or water-drop im-mediately after its formation from two smaller droplets fus-

ing together. In the case of ordinary liquid droplets, the
vibrations resulting from such fusion will quickly die out due
to the internal friction of liquids. In the case of the droplets
of nuclear fluid, in which the internal friction forces are com-

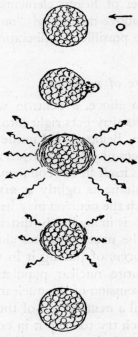

Fig. 26. Radiative capture of an incident neutron by an atomic nucleus.
After the neutron is pulled in by cohesive forces, strong vibrations of the
nucleus result in gamma radiation which gradually takes away the excess
of energy. When all the energy is radiated the nucleus comes to rest with
one extra-neutron in its structure.

pletely absent, but which, on the other hand, carry electric
charges, the dissipation of energy is usually taken care of by
the short-wave electromagnetic radiation, known as *gamma-
rays*, which is produced by rapidly vibrating nuclear charges.
It has been calculated that the energy of several million elec-

trons volts, representing the usual energy excesses encountered in various nuclear transformations, can be taken away by the gamma-radiation in about 0.000000000000001 second. Since however, an excited nucleus makes about 1,000,000,000,000,-000,000,000 vibrations per second, it still manages to make several million separate vibrations before it finally comes to rest. While the nucleus is thus vibrating after swallowing the neutron, there is still a chance for one or another nuclear particle to collect some of the surplus energy and to escape from the nucleus. Nuclear protons cannot do it very well since in order to leave the nucleus they must cross the barrier of electric force, which makes it just as difficult for them to get out as to get in. But neutrons can do it quite easily provided they have the necessary energy, and it happens quite often that the same neutrons whose entrance into the nucleus caused all the excitation, or one of his comrades (though, properly speaking, you cannot tell one neutron from another) is lucky enough to get out of the nucleus before the trap is closed. It will probably escape with less energy than it had when it entered, but it *can* get out, and can fly happily through space heading for an encounter with another nucleus. In considering the chances for a neutron which came into a nucleus to get out again, we can say that these chances are comparatively good if it was a fast neutron, and drop practically to zero if, before being caught, the neutron was moving at a crippling speed.* There is a way to prove this statement mathematically, but in consideration of the reader, we shall just use an easy analogy—a golf ball on the green. If, even though aiming correctly, you hit the hall too hard it will most likely jump the hole and roll over on the other side, whereas a gentle stroke gets the ball to where it belongs.

* It may be mentioned here, to avoid misunderstanding, that in the world of nuclei we have different standards of speed. A neutron is moving fast if it makes many thousand miles per second, whereas the speed of only a mile per second is considered as very low.

Now we can visualize the entire picture of what happens when a beam of fast neutrons passes through the material of the target (Fig. 27). Without experiencing the slightest difficulty and without losing any energy, the neutrons of the beam will piece the electronic envelopes of the atoms and only the nuclei which are directly in their way will be able to

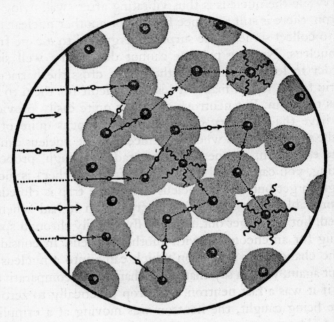

Fig. 27.

challenge their wild flight. But even the first four collisions with nuclei will in no way spell captivity for our fast neutrons, since in most cases they will get out of the nucleus again, suffering only a slight loss of energy and moving, after each collision, in a direction different from the one they had before. Thus the original beam of fast neutrons will be gradually slowed down and partially diffused or scattered. But, as the neutrons are gradually losing their velocity, their chances to escape capture in the next collision with a nucleus are rapidly decreasing and sooner or later they will all be swallowed up by the nuclei of the target material.

Since a gradual slowing down of fast neutrons by collisions with the atomic nuclei of the target material, leading to their final capture, requires quite a number of collisions, a beam of fast neutrons can penetrate deep into the material of the target, and if the latter is not very thick many neutrons will get through, escaping on the other side. For many purposes it is often desirable to use the beams of slow neutrons which will be captured practically in their very first encounter with the nuclei of the target. Since the neutrons kicked out of the nuclei by atomic bombardment always possess comparatively high velocities, methods must be worked out to slow the neutrons down before letting them into the target material. This can be done by passing a beam of fast neutrons through some very light substances as, for example, hydrogen, in which the slowing-down process is particularly effective. Because of the equality of masses of the incident neutron and the hydrogen nuclei (protons) with which it collides, the neutron will lose about half of its energy in each collision. In order to reduce the initial high energy of a neutron, amounting usually to several crocodiles, to the value of only 0.04 microcrocodiles, which corresponds to the energy of thermal motion at normal temperature, our neutron needs to experience only 27 consecutive collisions with hydrogen atoms. In fact, since each collision reduces the energy of the neutron by a factor of about two, 27 collisions will reduce it by $2^{27} = 10^8$, which is just the ratio between the initial and the desired final energies.

It must be remembered that, while a fast neutron is being slowed down by a number of collisions with protons, there is always a chance that one of these collisions will result in

capture of the neutron by the proton and the formation of
the nucleus of heavy hydrogen (deuteron). Experimental
evidence shows, however, that the chances of this latter process are comparatively small, so that after being slowed down
our neutron still can make well over a hundred elastic collisions with the hydrogen-nuclei before the capture finally
occurs.

3. *The result of neutron-capture.*

In carrying out his pioneering experiments on neutron-
bombardment, the Italian physicist *Enrico Fermi* noticed that
many materials subjected to such a bombardment became
radioactive, and emitted electrons for a long time after the
target was removed from under the beam. In order to understand this result, we must remember that the capture of a neutron by the nuclei of the target material leads in general to
the formation of the heavier isotope of the substance used.
Thus, for example, a neutron which clings to a nucleus of
ordinary carbon with the atomic weight 12, forms the heavier
carbon-isotope with atomic weight 13 (a well-known isotope
which, as we have already mentioned, is always present in
small amount in ordinary carbon). In a similar way, the main
isotope of iron with atomic weight 56, turns, after capturing
a neutron, into another rarer isotope of iron with atomic
weight 57. The nuclei produced in the above two examples
are stable, well-behaved nuclei, and their presence in the material subjected to neutron-bombardment could be noticed
only by analyzing this material by the mass-spectrographic
method. Even this would be extremely difficult if not out-
right impossible since the number of such nuclei produced in
ordinary neutron-bombardment is extremely small.

But let us see what happens if a neutron is captured by a
nucleus which already represents the heaviest existing isotope
of the bombarded material. Take for example ordinary so-

dium, all atoms of which have the weight 23, or manganese formed by identical atoms all with the weight 55. When a neutron is captured by one of these nuclei according to the symbolic equations:

$$_{11}Na^{23} + _{0}n^{1} \rightarrow {}_{11}Na^{24} + \text{gamma-ray}$$
$$_{25}Mn^{55} + _{0}n^{1} \rightarrow {}_{25}Mn^{56} + \text{gamma-ray}$$

We obtain the isotopes of these two elements which do not exist in nature being apparently unstable. The reason for instability of such nuclei lies in the much too high percentage of neutrons contained in their structure. An ordinary sodium nucleus contains 11 protons and 12 neutrons which apparently makes just a fine balance. However, when one more neutron is captured by this nucleus, the preponderance of neutrons over protons becomes too large for nuclear tranquility!

The way to reestablish the internal equilibrium can evidently be found in turning one of the nuclear neutrons (of which there are too many) into a proton (of which there are not enough). This is possible principally because neutrons and protons represent just two different electric modifications of the same fundamental nuclear particle, *the nucleon,* and can be transformed into one another by losing or acquiring electric charges. In order that a neutron can turn into a proton it must emit a portion of negative electricity, i.e., an electron, since the loss of a negative electric charge is equivalent to the acquiring of a positive one. Thus the unstable nucleus of sodium 24 formed by neutron bombardment, will emit an electron turning into a nucleus with the same mass but with the charge of 12 positive units. It is no longer a nucleus of sodium since having the charge 12 it now will be surrounded by an envelope of 12 electrons thus forming an atom of the element known as magnesium. Looking into the table of stable isotopes we find, in fact, that there exists in nature a stable isotope of magnesium with atomic weight 24; it forms about 78 percent of ordinary magnesium, the rest being equally distributed between the isotopes Mg^{25} and Mg^{26}. In a similar way we find that the instability of a heavy manganese isotope produced by neutron-capture also results in an electron-emission leading to the formation of the iron-isotope Fe^{56} which constitutes about 91 per cent of ordinary iron. The two reactions described above can be written in the form of symbolic equations:

$$_{11}Na^{24} \rightarrow {}_{12}Mg^{24} + \bar{e}$$
$$_{25}Mn^{56} \rightarrow {}_{26}Fe^{56} + \bar{e}$$

where $\bar{e}$ stands for the negative electron emitted in this transformation.

When the capture of a neutron disturbs the internal balance of the nucleus, the transformation leading to the emission of a nuclear electron does not, however, take place immediately since the process of loosening the electric charge from a nuclear particle is generally a rather slow process. This process is essentially of a statistical nature. Different nuclei eject their electrons at different moments over a certain period of time, the intensity of this emission gradually decreasing as indicated in Fig. 28. It is customary to characterize such dyng out emission-processes by their "half-life" which corresponds to the time period during which the process goes half way through.

In the two cases discussed above the electric readjustment of the nucleus takes place in 4.8 hours for activated sodium, and in 2.6 hours for manganese. In some instances the half-life periods of induced activity are much longer: thus the electron-emission of activated sulphur lasts on an average for 88 days, that of activated cobalt for 5.3 years, and the activity induced in a heavier carbon isotope has a mean-life of about ten thousand years.

It must be added here that the neutron-capture does not represent the only way of producing the artificial radioactive elements since a similar phenomenon takes place when the nucleus captures an incident proton. In this case the situation is, however, reversed since after such a capture, protons and not neutrons are in plurality. Thus the electric adjustment must be accomplished by transformation of one of the protons into a neutron and the emission of a *positive* electron. A typ-

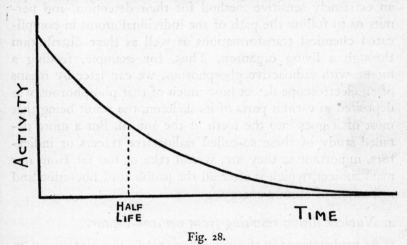

Fig. 28.

ical case of such a process is represented by proton-capture in a carbon-nucleus resulting in the formation of an unstable nucleus of nitrogen. It can be represented by the easily understandable symbolic equations:

$$_6C^{12} + {}_1H^1 \rightarrow {}_7N^{13} + \text{gamma-ray}$$
$$_7N^{13} \rightarrow {}_6C^{13} + \overset{+}{e}$$

the induced positive electron-activity having a half-life of ten minutes.

However, owing to the barrier of electric force which prevents the penetration of protons into the heavily charged nuclei, processes of such a kind could be produced only in the case of the light elements. Thus the number of the positively-active elements, or *Curie-Joliot* elements, is considerably smaller than that of the *Fermi* elements with negative-electron activity. The artificial radioactive elements produced by neutron-bombardment find a great many useful applications in various branches of chemistry and especially in biology. In fact, the radioactivity of these elements supplies us with an extremely sensitive method for their detection, and permits us to follow the path of the individual atoms in complicated chemical transformations as well as their distribution through a living organism. Thus, for example, feeding a mouse with radioactive phosphorous, we can later by means of an electroscope detect how much of that phosphorous was deposited in various parts of its skeleton, the result being that most of it goes into the teeth of the animal. But a more detailed study of these so-called radioactive tracers or indicators, important as they are, would take us too far from our main subject, which is after all the problem of liberation and utilization of atomic energy.

4. *Nuclear fission resulting from neutron-capture.*

As we have seen in the previous sections, the entrance of an incident neutron into the atomic nucleus usually results in its capture and the reemission of the excess-energy, set free by the capture process, in the form of gamma-radiation. However, in the case of very heavy nuclei the capture of a neutron may also lead to the fission-process since in this case the energy necessary to produce the critical deformation of the nucleus may become less than the energy brought in by the neutron. (Fig. 29). In fact, the energy received by the nucleus in the capture-process is composed of about five crocodiles delivered by cohesive forces which pull the neutron in, plus whatever value of kinetic energy the neutron may have had before meeting the nucleus. Looking at Fig. 14 (Ch. I), which represents the critical deformation-energies for the nuclei of different elements, we find that, having very large values for the lightest element which are unstable in regard to fission, the activation energy comes down to the values of

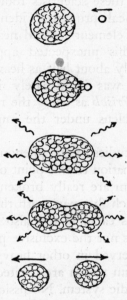

Fig. 29. Nuclear fission produced by the process of neutron-capture. If the energy brought in by the captured neutron is larger than the critical deformation-energy of the nucleus, the very first vibration will bring the nucleus over the stability limit, and it will break up into two halves which fly apart at high speed.

only about five crocodiles for the elements near the upper end of the periodic system. Thus we may expect that for the heaviest existing chemical elements the energy of neutron-capture alone or with the addition of few crocodiles of kinetic energy, would be enough to deform the nucleus beyond the critical limit causing its breaking up into two halves.

The above considerations represent the explanation of the phenomenon of the nuclear fission of heavy elements under neutron-bombardment, which was discovered by *O. Hahn* and *F. Strassman* in Germany late in 1938. In studying various radioactive products formed in uranium under the action of a neutron-beam, these scientists found that one of these products has chemical properties identical with those of barium which is an element located near the middle of the periodic system. This unexpected appearance of barium atoms, which are only about half as heavy as the bombarded atoms of uranium, was immediately interpreted by *Lise Meitner* and *O. R. Frisch* as being the result of the splitting of the uranium nucleus under the impact of an incident neutron.

Further detailed studies of the phenomenon gave complete experimental confirmation to this point of view, showing that the nuclei of uranium are really broken up into two nearly equal fragments which fly apart with the terrific energies of a hundred crocodiles each. It was also found that the phenomenon of fission is not the exclusive property of uranium, but can be also observed in other heavy elements like protactinium and thorium which are located next to uranium at the end of the periodic system. No fission produced by neutron-bombardment was observed for other heavy elements, such as bismuthum, lead, mercury, or gold, a fact which as we know now should be ascribed not to the absence of metastability in these nuclei, but rather to the fact that neutrons with only few crocodiles of kinetic energy, like those used in the experiments, were not able to bring these nuclei over the threshold of their metastable state.

An extremely important question in the study of nuclear fission in various heavy elements, is the question whether their fission requires the bombardment by neutrons of rather high energy, or whether it would occur just as readily if one used slow neutrons with practically no kinetic energy at all. To realize the importance of this question we must remember that fast neutrons have only a very little chance to be captured by the nucleus in which they enter, and usually escape again and again, losing each time a small part of their original kinetic energy. Thus when a beam of fast neutrons enters into the material, only very few of them will have the "bad luck" to be captured and to produce fission while still moving fast. Most of the neutrons in the beam will be going in and coming out of the nuclei which they encounter on their way, until practically all their original energy is dissipated in a large number of these casual encounters. When the neutrons are good and ready, moving quite slowly between the surrounding atoms, they represent an easy prey to the first nucleus which they meet, but . . .

But if the capture of the slow neutron does not excite the nucleus sufficiently to bring it over the threshold of metastability, these will be only radiative captures without even one single case of fission. Thus *if the nuclei of the substance bombarded by neutrons require for their fission an energy larger than that delivered by cohesive forces alone, very few fission-processes will actually take place, since the fast neutrons would not do it, whereas the slowed-down neutrons cannot.*

The careful study of the fission process in different heavy elements using neutrons of varying velocity revealed an important fact: *that neither thorium, nor protactinium, nor in the main isotope of uranium: U-238 (which forms 99.3 per cent of natural uranium), show any fission when slow neutrons are used.* Apparently in all these elements the critical deformation energy is somewhat larger than the vibrational energy of the nucleus resulting from the capture of a slow neutron, so that they break only if hit by a fast neutron which carries additional kinetic energy. Thus, for example, according to *Niels Bohr* and *J. A. Wheeler* splitting the nucleus of thorium requires seven crocodiles, whereas the capture of a slow neutron delivers only five. Similarly in uranium-238, six crocodiles are needed for fission and only five are liberated in the slow neutron capture. Consequently in order to produce the fission of these two nuclear species we must use neutrons with the kinetic energy of over two and over one crocodiles respectively. *The only brand of nuclei existing in Nature in which the critical fission energy is so low that a slow-neutron capture results in fission are the nuclei of the rarer uranium-isotope: U-235 which is present in the natural uranium in the extremely small amount of 0.7 per cent.** Indeed, in this case the capture of a slow neutron supplies the nucleus with the energy of six crocodiles, whereas only five are needed to cause the fission.

Since, as we shall see later, the ability of nuclei to be split by slow neutrons represents a necessary condition for the possibility of neutron-multiplication process, this *rare isotope of uranium (U-235) represents the only natural substance which can be used for the purposes of large-scale liberation of atomic energy.*

In Fig. 30 we give a schematic picture of comparative energy-balance in the fission processes of various heavy elements, using for this purpose the analogy of the volcano discussed in the first chapter of this book. The distance from the bottom of the crater to zero-level (which is lost in clouds down below) represents the total energy which can be set free when the nucleus breaks into two halves, whereas the

* It must be remembered that U-235 does not actually belong to the radioactive family of uranium, as can be seen from Table II at the end of the book. U-235 or actino-uranium, as it is properly called, represents the head of the actinium family and goes over into protactinium by emitting an alpha-particle. The comparatively short mean-life of actino-uranium (U-235) which is only four hundred million years, accounts for its extreme rarity in nature as was discussed in the previous section. Being an isotope of ordinary uranium, actino-uranium is always present with uranium in all uranium containing minerals.

depth of the crater itself represents the activation-energy which must be given to the nucleus in order to cause fission. The vertical black arrows in the picture correspond to the energy which is given to the nucleus as the result of a slow-neutron capture. Where the black arrow does not reach the top of the crater, the captured energy is not enough, and the fission in these elements can be produced only by fast neutrons. On the other hand, where the arrow sticks out, the fission with slow neutrons is possible. We see from this

Fig. 30. Mountain landscape illustrating the problem of nuclear fission.

mountain landscape that whereas in three mountains on the left the black arrow is hidden inside the crater, it sticks a little out of the crater for the mountain marked: "Actino-uranium" alias U-235.

But what is this still higher peak on the extreme right which shows a much larger energy-liberation and also better fission conditions? And who are those people carrying the building materials up the slope, and spoiling the quiet beauty of the mountains? The name on this peak says "Plutonium," and you will not find it in any textbook of chemistry. Well, this is a new element with the atomic number *94,* one of the so-called "trans-uranium-elements" which does not exist in nature but can be built only by artificial methods. We shall discuss in the later sections of this chapter the ways and means by which this new element can be produced, and will satisfy ourselves here with the remark that plutonium represents the parent of actino-uranium, and is transformed into it through the emission of an alpha-particle:

$$_{94}Pu^{239} \rightarrow {}_{92}U^{235} + {}_2He^4$$

Properly speaking, it is plutonium and not actino-uranium who is the head of actinium family. But, not having a very strong constitution, i.e., having a comparatively short mean-life of only a few tens of thousands of years, this element has completely decayed during the billions of years which have elapsed since the chemical elements were formed. Thus actino-uranium (U-235) is the legitimate *active head* of its family, although it may have in its genealogical picture gallery not only its dead father "Sir Plutonium" but also quite a number of earlier predecessors which belong to the great but comparatively short-lived generation of the transuranium elements. All, or at least most, members of this past generation of chemical elements can be expected to be fissionable in a bigger and better way than their remaining offspring, the dying-out actino-uranium. And calling back to life these fission-giants of the past, which is now being done by stuffing the smaller bodies of the nuclei of today with extra neutrons, we can obtain a considerable display of metastable elements which can be used for bombs and many other things. However, it must not be forgotten that in order to build transuranium elements we must have plenty of neutrons, and a large number of netutrons can at present be produced only by fission of U-235. Thus one can revive the predecessors of U-235 only at the expense of its own life.

5. The Fission-Fragments.

In the previous discussion we have tacitly assumed that in the process of fission the nucleus always break up into two equal halves. This is not necessarily so since, even in the case of ordinary mercury droplets, the breaking-up process may depend on the way in which the blow is delivered. In the same way we may expect that in the case of nuclear fission a slight variation in the size of two fragments may occur depending, for example, on whether the incident neutron delivers a head-on or only a sidewise impact.

But there is also another, more important reason for the uneven breaking-up of the nucleus. The point is that neutrons and protons forming any given nucleus are united inside it in certain structural subgroups, the particles of the same subgroup being somewhat more strongly bound between themselves than with the other particles of the same nucleus. The existence of such subgroups, containing from one to several dozen particles each, shows itself in a certain periodicity of various nuclear properties (relative number of neutrons and protons, total binding energy, etc.) along the natural system of elements. The grouping of particles inside the nucleus is analogous, though considerably less strongly expressed, to the formation of electronic shells in atomic envelopes, which is, as well known, responsible for the periodicity of chemical properties of the elements. When a heavy nucleus is ready to go through the process of fission, it may easily occur that the division into two exactly equal parts would require the breaking-up of one of the subgroups which is more difficult to do than to break the separate subgroups apart. In this case, just as in the case of a material object glued together from several parts, the cleavage will most probably run along the line of the least resistance, and the nucleus will be broken up into two not quite equal parts (Fig. 31). This is apparently what happens in the case of splitting the uranium nucleus which, according to *Hahn* and *Strassmann*, results in the formation of the radioactive barium isotope. In fact, the weight of a radioactive barium atom is probably about 140 * which is considerably larger than one half of 236 which represents the weight of an actino-uranium atom after the capture of a neutron. If one of the fragments weighs 140, the other must weigh 96 and looking into the table of elements we find that this weight corresponds to an isotope of zirconium. Thus in this case the two fragments take respectively 59

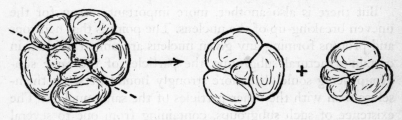

Fig. 31. Why a nucleus containing several subgroups of particles does not necessarily break up into two equal parts. Of course, this figure gives only a suggestion of the actual situation in the nucleus. In fact, different subgroups in the nuclei are not separated, but penetrate through each other like members of different political parties in a country.

and 41 percent of the original mass, with the possible additional variations caused by the circumstances of collision with the neutron which caused the fission.

We now come to another important fact about the fission-fragments, namely that they are always overcharged with negative electricity and are therefore subject to the process of consequent electron-emission. In fact, when the nucleus of U-236 breaks into two parts with respective masses 140 and

* The regular atomic weight of stable barium is 138. But, as we shall see later, the fragments of uranium fission must have an excess of neutrons thus having somewhat higher weight than normally. The active barium atom $_{56}Ba^{140}$ would emit two electrons going over into the stable nucleus of cerium $_{58}Ce^{140}$.

96, the electric charge of the original nucleus must be also divided between the two fragments. If we divide the charge of 92 between the fragments in proportion to their masses we get 54 for the heavier fragment, and 38 for the lighter one. These atomic numbers correspond to the chemical elements known as xenon and strontium. However, looking in the table of the stable isotopes (printed at the end of the book) we find neither xenon with atomic weight 140 nor strontium with atomic weight 96. Since the above weights correspond to the stable nuclei of cerium and zirconium with the nuclear charges of 58 and 40 units, our two fragments evidently must emit four and two negative electrons respectively to come down to an electrically balanced state. The entire process can be now summarized by a simple set of alchemical formulae:

Original fission process:

$$_{92}U^{235} + _{0}n^{1} \rightarrow _{54}Xe^{140} + _{38}Sr^{96}$$

Subsequent electric adjustments:

$$_{54}Xe^{140} \rightarrow _{55}Cs^{140} + \text{electron}$$
$$_{55}Cs^{140} \rightarrow _{56}Ba^{140} + \text{electron}$$
$$_{56}Ba^{140} \rightarrow _{57}La^{140} + \text{electron}$$
$$_{57}La^{140} \rightarrow _{58}Ce^{140} + \text{electron}$$
$$_{58}Ce^{140} = \text{stable nucleus}$$
$$_{38}Sr^{96} \rightarrow _{39}Y^{96} + \text{electron}$$
$$_{39}Y^{96} \rightarrow _{40}Zr^{96} + \text{electron}$$
$$_{40}Zr^{96} = \text{stable nucleus}$$

While the fission itself takes place instantaneously, the subsequent electric adjustments may take quite a long time and are responsible for the remaining activity (electron-emission) of the materials subjected to fission. As we have seen above, the discovery of the fission-process itself was due to the presence of radioactive barium which corresponds to the intermediate adjustment stage in the heavier fragment of uranium-fission.

The fact that the fission of heavy nuclei always leads to negatively super-charged fragments, can be simply understood if we remember that the relative number of neutrons and protons corresponding to an electric equilibrium changes with the increasing atomic weight in favor of neutrons. In fact, whereas in the nuclei of light elements we have equal numbers of these particles (for example 8 neutrons and 8 protons in oxygen), the ratio is $\frac{60}{47} = 1.27$ for silver, $\frac{118}{79} = 1.50$ for gold, and $\frac{146}{92} = 1.60$ for uranium.* When a heavy nucleus breaks up into two fragments, each fragment will evidently have the same percentage of neutrons as it corresponds to the original nucleus, whereas its smaller mass actually requires a smaller percentage. Thus, some of the neutrons inside the fragment must turn into protons, emitting positive electrons. This adjustment process is, of course, very similar to that observed in the so-called Fermi elements which originate through the radiative neutron-capture in the lighter nuclei.

6. *The Fission-neutrons.*

If the formation of two radioactive fragments were the only result of the nuclear fission-process, this process could not be any more useful for the solution of the problem of large scale release of atomic energy than the ordinary methods of atomic bombardment by electrically accelerated charged projectiles. It is true of course that in each individual fission process the incident neutron releases two hundred crocodiles of energy which is ten times more than the largest energy

---

* This relative decrease in the number of protons in the heavier nuclei is due to the fact that because of the mutual electric repulsion between these particles the large number of them in the nucleus becomes "undesirable" from the point of view of nuclear equilibrium.

release in any other nuclear reaction heretofore observed.*
But in producing free neutrons by the painstaking method
of atomic bombardment we need to spend a grand total of
several thousand crocodiles of energy † to get just one
neutron. The procedure evidently does not pay!

In spite of the fact that the heavy fission-fragments carry
a much larger energy than it was ever before observed in
nuclear experiments, they are quite unable to produce any
further disintegration. Because of their high electric charge,
fission-fragments will very rapidly lose their initial velocities
by the process of electron-friction in the atomic envelopes
through which they fly, and by the time they encounter a
nucleus, they will not have enough energy to come close
to it against the strong forces of electric repulsion.

But the fact is that, *apart from the two heavy fragments,
the fission of an atomic nucleus also results in the formation
of several (between 2 and 3) smaller fragments which are
simply fast flying neutrons.* There are several different ways
in which neutrons can be produced in the process of nuclear
fission. First of all we may very well expect that during the
violent breaking-up of the nuclear droplet, some of the
particles, which cannot make up their minds which of the
two fragments to join, will fly apart all by themselves forming a miniature splash of nuclear fluid (Fig. 32a). Another
possibility is that these neutrons are not emitted in the process
of fission itself, but escape from the two fission-fragments
some time after their separation (Fig. 32b). In fact, we must
expect that immediately after their formation, the two frag-

* The largest energy released by the method of atomic bombardment
was observed when a beam of deuterons (heavy hydrogen) was directed
on Li^6 or B^{11} targets. We get in these cases respectively 22 and 19.5 crocodiles.

† This number represents the collective energy of all the charged projectiles needed to make one lucky hit on a nucleus thus releasing one
neutron.

ments find themselves in an extremely excited state, vibrating like two pieces of a steel spring which have just been broken in two halfs. Since the fragments are already below the critical size for fission, and would not break up no matter how strongly they vibrate, this energy must be dissipated by the emission of gamma-radiation. However, before the fragment

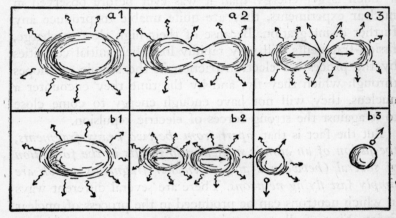

Fig. 32. *Emission of splash neutrons (a) and shortly delayed neutrons (b) as the result of nuclear fission.* a1. Nucleus is vibrating and emitting gamma rays; a2. Preparations for fission are made; a3. Nucleus breaks in two with some stray neutrons flying away; b1. Same as a1; b2. Nucleus breaks up clearly in two parts which are vibrating and emitting gamma-rays; b3. Neutrons are escaping from still vibrating fragments. One of the fragments has lost all its energy and has come to rest.

loses all its energy by radiation, this energy can be picked up by one or the other of its structural neutrons that want to make their getaway from the nucleus (Fig. 33). These escape-neutrons can be expected to have just enough energy to break loose from the cohesive forces which would not let them go, but, since the fragments from which they escape are moving very fast, they will also acquire a high speed, in the very same way as a man jumping from a fast moving train. It goes without saying that although these neutrons are emitted after the fission, the actual delay is very short. In fact we know that the gamma-radiation takes not more than 0.0000000000000001 seconds to drain all the energy out of an excited nucleus, so that the escape-neutrons must be emitted within this short time-interval. Because of the extremely high excitation of fission-fragments and the large

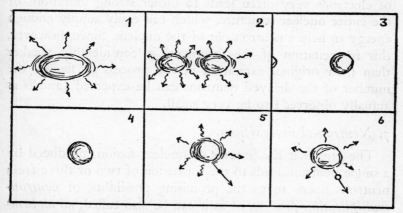

Fig. 33. *Emission of long-delayed neutrons.* 1. Nucleus vibrating. 2. Nucleus breaks in two, each fragment vibrating. 3. Fragment has come to rest. 4. Fragment still at rest. 5. The emission of an electron re-excites the fragment, and the gamma-ray emission begins again. 6. A long-delayed neutron is finally emitted.

amount of energy available, the cases of electron-escape seem to take place rather often. If, as is very likely, most of the observed fission neutrons originate this way, there must be one or two escape-cases in each fragment.

We cannot finish this section without mentioning the *delayed, or rather long-delayed neutrons* which come out several seconds or even a minute after the fission is completed. Since the original excitation of fragments produced in the fission-process cannot possibly last so long, the origin of these delayed neutrons must be ascribed to the re-excitation of the fragments taking place at a considerably later date. The reason for such delayed re-excitation can easily be found in the fact that the fission fragments must go through the process of internal electric adjustment (see previous section) which is in general a rather slow process. We also know that the electric readjustment of nuclei followed by the emission of electrons very often leads to rather strong vibrations of the entire nuclear structure, which can easily supply enough energy to help a neutron out of the nucleus. Since, however, this re-excitation of the fragments is considerably weaker than their original excitation in the process of fission, the number of the delayed neutrons can be expected (and is as actually observed) to be very small.

7. Neutron-chain-reactions.

The fact that the process of nuclear fission, produced by a single neutron, leads to the formation of two or three fresh neutrons opens to us the promising possibility of *neutron-multiplication-process*, or as it can be also called, an *alchemical chain-reaction*. Indeed, if each of several neutrons produced in a single process will in their turn cause the fission, more fresh neutrons will be produced resulting in a still larger number of subsequent fissions (Fig. 34). Thus our neutrons will multiply with each generation like rabbits on a farm, and in a very short time their number will become tremendously high.* Of course, just as in the case of rabbits,

---

* The above-described chain-reaction-process also plays an important role in ordinary chemical transformations of the metastable compounds. Thus we have seen in Ch. I (sec. 1) that the molecules of the metastable substance known as nitroglycerine can be broken into many fragments (Fig. 2) with the liberation of large amounts of molecular binding energy. The transition from the original molecule of nitroglycerine into the molecules of water, carbondioxide, and nitrogen, takes place however in a number of steps following the general pattern of the chain-reaction. It may start with one single process in which, owing to strong thermal

the necessary condition for the growth of neutron popula-
tion is that each neutron-parent of any given generation will
produce on the average more than one neutron-offspring of
the next generation.

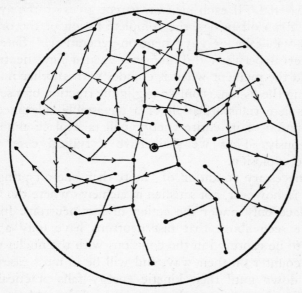

Fig. 34. Five consecutive steps in the development of a chain-reaction
with the branching-ratio: 2.

Thus, for example, if each neutron-parent has on the
average two neutron-offsprings, the population will double
with each generation, and everybody knows how fast such

vibrations of one of the molecules, one of its peripheral NO_2 groups bends
so strong that oxygen atoms approach the atoms of carbon or hydrogen.
The formation of new bonds between these atoms sets free enough energy
to break up the molecule in several pieces. In particular the two remaining
NO_2-groups break loose and travel around attacking other molecules of
nitroglycerine. In each such encounter, oxygen from these traveling active
fragments unites with carbon or nitrogen of new molecules causing them
to break up in their turn. The number of free-traveling NO_2-groups increases in geometrical progression, and the process of chemical transformation runs faster and faster terminating in an explosion.

a multiplication-process goes. If we have one kilogram of heavy fissionable material which contains about 2.10^{24} separate nuclei, and let in just one neutron, it will need only 80 successive generations of neutron-breeding to consume the entire material.* If each neutron-parent gives on the average three neutron offsprings, the complete fission of the original material will take only 55 neutron-generations.* Since the time-interval between the moment when a new neutron is born and the moment when it collides with another nucleus, producing the fission, is only a negligible fraction of a second, the complete transformation of a metastable substance and the liberation of its entire energy will take place almost instantaneously. Thus we shall have a typical case of an alchemic explosion.

The necessary condition of "more-than-one-offspring-per-parent" is, however, not satisfied in elements where the fission takes place only under the action of fast neutrons. In fact, we have seen above that fast neutrons have only a small chance to be captured in the collisions with the nuclei which they encounter on their way, and will be in most cases only slowed down until their kinetic energy falls practically to zero. Since these exhausted neutrons, not being able to break the nuclei in which they enter, will finally be captured through the ordinary radiation process, the proportion of fission processes will be necessarily very small and the chain reaction will have no chance to develop. The above considerations rule out such elements as thorium, protactinium and the heavier uranium isotope as possible substances for the nuclear chain reactions, and leads us to the conclusion that *the only atomic nuclei which can be used for the large scale liberation of alchemic energy by the method of neutron-multiplication, are the nuclei of lighter uranium isotope 235.*

In natural uranium, where the active isotope U-235 is

* In fact $2^{80} = 2.10^{24}$ and $3^{55} = 2.10^{24}$.

strongly diluted by the inactive heavier isotope U-238, the process of neutron-multiplication is, of course, ruled out owing to the fact that most of the fission neutrons will be captured by heavier nuclei and thus taken out of the reaction. But in pure U-235 practically every neutron produced in fission will cause another fission, so that a single neutron entering this substance will lead to the instantaneous explosion.

If the above statement were absolutely true there would be no hope of ever obtaining a sample of pure U-235, since it would be immediately set off by the very first stray neutron entering into it. And there are plenty of these stray neutrons constantly flying around—being produced by cosmic rays, natural radioactivity of terrestrial materials, and so forth. The point is, however, that the condition for the neutron-multiplication-process requires not only that the neutrons produced in the fission are not uselessly absorbed by the process of radiative capture in the material in question, but also that they should not escape through the surface of the sample before they have a chance to produce another fission. After all, what is the use of the rapid breeding of rabbits, if most of the young ones manage to get through the old fence surrounding the farm and disappear into the woods before they even reach maturity? The possibility of neutron-escape through the surface of fissionable material leads to the notion of the *critical size of the sample* necessary for the neutron-chain reaction to develop in its interior. It is thus clear that if we have a sample of fissionable material, the diameter of which is smaller than the average distance which must be traveled by the fast neutron before it produces the fission process, no chain reaction will take place at all, since practically every single neutron produced inside the sample will escape through the surface before doing damage to any of the nuclei. If, on the other hand, we have a larger sample,

the situation becomes favorable for chain development, since
even when the fission takes place close to the surface, one
of the several fresh neutrons produced in it will probably be
directed inwards and will have a good chance of producing
further fission-processes while traveling through the thickness
of the charge. In order to estimate the distance which must
be traveled by a fast neutron before it can collide with the
uranium nucleus and produce fission, we must remember that
the radius of the uranium nucleus is equal to $0.9 \cdot 10^{-12}$ cm.
corresponding to the collision cross-section of $2.5 \cdot 10^{-24}$ cm^2.
Since one cubic centimeter of uranium contains about 4.10^{22}
nuclei, the combined nuclear cross-section corresponding to
a layer-thickness of 1 cm. will be $2.5 \cdot 10^{-24} \times 4 \times 10^{22} = 0.1$
cm^2. Thus a fast neutron must travel about 10 cm. through
solid uranium before it is able to produce fission. This leads to
the conclusion that the critical size of explosive Uranium-235
samples must be of the order of magnitude of 10 centimeters
which corresponds to the critical mass of a few tens of
kilograms. The conditions for chain-reactions in small samples
can be considerably improved by surrounding them with
a layer of inert material which has the property of reflecting
the neutrons escaping through the surface back into the
fissionable material. Such a reflecting layer, which scares
the runaway rabbits and forces them to crawl back through
the fence surrounding the farm, is technically known as a
reflector or *tamper*.

It must be remembered that, whereas the samples of fissionable material larger than the critical size are subject to instantaneous explosion, even in the samples of smaller size the
process of neutron-multiplication will go on, though in a
quiet and orderly way, gradually destroying the fissionable
nuclei and contaminating the material by the inactive products of the fission. Thus in order to preserve or, as they say,
"can" fissionable materials it is preferable to keep them in

quite small samples (thin layers), shielding these samples as well as possible from the stray neutrons originating from cosmic rays and the natural radioactivity of the various materials. The simplest method of shielding fissionable materials from stray neutrons is probably by placing them in cadmium containers and storing under water. In fact the water will slow down all incident neutrons to the thermal velocities, and cadmium, which is the best slow neutron absorber, will catch them before they have a chance to penetrate into the stored material.

8. *Separation of U-235 isotope.**

We have seen in the previous section that the only fissionable element existing in nature is U-235, and that it is always found only strongly diluted by U-238 which prevents the development of multiplicative nuclear-chain-reaction. Thus, in order to use the atomic power of U-235, we must either separate it from the heavier inert isotope, or devise some method by which the extinguishing effect of the heavier isotope on the chain-reaction in U-235 can be, at least to a certain extent, neutralized. The most direct way is, of course, that of isotope-separation which we shall discuss in the present section.

Since the isotopes of a given element possess identical chemical properties, it is evidently impossible to achieve their separation by any ordinary methods used in chemistry, so that one can rely only on various physical methods based on the mass-differences between two kinds of atoms. The most prominent among various possible physical methods is the

* This section, as well as the following two sections, are largely based on the material published in the official report by *H. D. Smyth:* "Atomic Energy for Military Purposes" (Aug. 1945). The reader is referred to the above report for the administrative history of the Atomic Bomb Project, as well as for the further technical details concerning the separation of U-235 isotope, and production of plutonium.

mass-spectrographic method which utilizes the deflection of ion-beams in a strong magnetic field. As we have seen in Chapter I, this was the method by which the existence of isotopes was first demonstrated, and this was also the method by which the first, though ridiculously small, quantities of U-235 were first obtained. In fact, in 1940, by using an ordinary mass spectrograph, *A. O. Nier* was able to separate 0.000,000,001 gram of the lighter uranium isotope which was used for direct experimental proof that it is U-235 which is responsible for the fission of natural uranium by slow neutrons.

The main disadvantage of the electro-magnetic separation method lies in the difficulty of producing strong beams of fast-moving ions, and in the fact that when such beams carrying heavy concentration of charged particles are produced they have the tendency to spread out fan-wise under the forces of the mutual electric repulsion between the ions. This second difficulty was considered as absolutely prohibitive for the use of the beam-deflection method for any large-scale separation of the uranium-isotopes, until, in the fall of 1941, the solution of this difficulty was finally found by *E. O. Lawrence*, the inventor of the cyclotron. By using this device, the nature of which cannot be revealed at present, Lawrence and his collaborators were able to construct the magnetic mass separator which received the name of *Calutron* (California-University-tron) and is represented schematically in Fig. 35. It consists of an ion-source in which the positively charged atoms of uranium are produced by strong electric discharge through the vapor of uranium-salts; a large magnet which deflects the ion-beam, and a collector in which the separated isotopes are accumulated. By using the magnetic field of the giant 184-inch electromagnet of the University of California, Lawrence was able to separate one microgram (0.0000001 gm) of U-235 per hour. Though at this rate it would take a billion hours or a hundred thousand years to produce one kilogram (2 pounds) of pure U-235, the method was sufficiently promising and was subject to further improvements. Thus it was adopted by the United States Government as one of the practical methods for separation of uranium-isotope, and a large production-plant consisting of

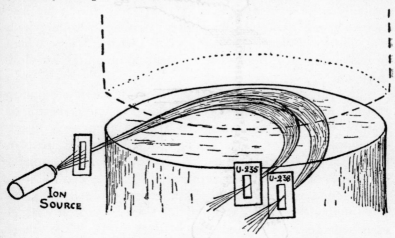

Fig. 35. The scheme of the *Calutron* for magnetic separation of isotopes. A beam of ions produced in the ion-source enters into the magnetic field between two poles of a giant electromagnet. Since the lighter atoms of U-235 are now more strongly deflected than the heavier atoms of U-238, the beam separates into two parts, thus permitting the collection of the lighter isotope.

a large number of separate calutron-units was built at the secret site in the Tennessee Valley now known as the *Clinton Engineer Works*. This plant, the construction of which was of course far from being simple and inexpensive, was authorized in November 1942, began operating exactly a year later, and was the first to supply large quantities of pure U-235 for use in the atomic bomb.

Another interesting electric method of isotope separation

is based on the uses of oscillating electric fields which make
the ion-beams dance in the very same way as the electrons
dance in the amplifier-tubes when some famous crooner sings

Fig. 36. The scheme of the *Isotron* for electric separation of isotopes. A
beam of ions from the source passes through an alternate electric field between the source and a net placed in the way of the beam. Since lighter
atoms are more accelerated than heavier ones by the electric field of a
given strength, the successive electric impulses will produce in the beam
a stratification in which each successive stratum is alternatively richer in
U-235 and U-238. When this stratified beam passes through the horizontal
electric field which is synchronized with the field producing the stratification, the strata enriched with U-235 will be deflected to the right, and those
with U-238 to the left.

on the radio. The ion-separator based on this principle was
built by *H. D. Smyth* and *R. R. Wilson* in Princeton and is
known under the name of *isotron*. It is represented schematically in Fig. 36, and the principle of its operation is described

in the subscript to the picture. It is possible that the future development of the isotron will make it a competitor of the Calutron which is now the principal apparatus for uranium-isotope separation.

While the action of electro-magnetic mass-separators such as calutrons or isotrons is based on the individual action of electric and magnetic fields on the moving ions of the beam, there is another group of so-called *statistical methods* which

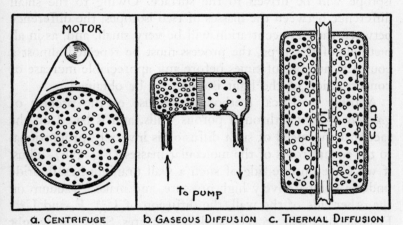

a. CENTRIFUGE   b. GASEOUS DIFFUSION   c. THERMAL DIFFUSION

Fig. 37. Three "statistical" methods of isotope-separation.

utilizes only the average behavior of large groups of atoms with different mass. We shall discuss here several of the most important methods of this kind.

One method is known as *centrifugal* and utilizes the principle often used in techniques for separation of two fractions with different density (Fig. 37a). If a mixture of two such materials is placed in a cylindrical vessel and subjected to rapid rotation, the heavier fraction driven by the centrifugal force will accumulate near the outer walls, whereas the lighter fraction collects closer to the center. If, for example, we put ordinary milk in such a separator, the heavier liquid will be pushed to the periphery and the lighter globula of butter will collect in the central part, practically ready to be spread on a piece of bread.

Similarly, centrifuging some gaseous uranium compound, as for example, uranium-hexafluoride, we can expect that the molecules containing the light uranium isotope will concentrate near the center whereas those containing the heavier isotope will be driven to the surface. Owing to the small difference between the masses of two isotopes, the difference between their concentration will be very small, and, as in all methods of this type, the process must be repeated almost a countless number of times before any appreciable increase of concentration of the light isotope can be obtained.

Another statistical method makes use of the process of *gaseous diffusion* through porous walls, and is based on the fact that the speed of such diffusion is inversely proportional to the square roots of the molecular masses (Fig. 37b). Thus, if we place on one side of such a wall uranium-hexafluoride under a comparatively high pressure, and make a vacuum on the other side of the wall, the diffusion of $U^{238} F_6$-and $U^{235} F_6$-molecules will proceed at different rates. Since the weight of the above two molecules are respectively 352 and 349, the ratio of their diffusion-velocities will be:

$$\sqrt{\frac{352}{349}} = 1.0043$$

which also represents the increase in the concentration of the lighter isotope. If we want to increase the concentration, say, by a factor of 2, we must repeat the operation again and again, x times where x satisfies the relation $(1.0043)^x = 2$. From this we obtain: $x = 160$ for the number of operations needed. Taking into account the large amount of material which must be put through these successive operations, and the slowness of the diffusion process we see that this is a rather lengthy, though not at all impossible, process. A large gaseous-diffusion plant, based on the preliminary research of *J. R. Dunning* and *H. C. Urey* in Columbia University, was also built at Clinton Engineer Works in Tennessee Valley utilizing thousands of pumps and acres of porous walls through which uranium-hexafluoride was sent.

The third statistical method of isotope separation is based on the principle of thermal *diffusion* (Fig. 37c). It was known for quite a while that the existence of temperature gradient in a mixture of two gases results in the tendency of one type of the molecules to concentrate in the hotter region and the other type in the colder region. This tendency which depends in general both on the chemical nature of the molecules as well as on their weight, will depend only on the weight for the mixture of $U^{238} F_6$ and $U^{235} F_6$ molecules since their chemical properties are exactly the same. The mass-separator base of thermal diffusion can be imagined in principle as a long vertical cylinder cooled from outside, with a hot wire running along its axis. As the result of thermal diffusion the heavier isotope will concentrate near the cooler outer wall, while the lighter one will tend to collect closer to the hot wire. On the other hand, the cold gas near the wall will sink, and the hot gas near the wire will rise, thus creating a convection current similar to that observed in the famous Russian samovar. The interaction of these two phenomena is extremely complicated and only very few people understand what actually happens. (The author is not one of them!) But the fact remains that the whole thing *does* lead to the partial separation of isotopes, and a plant of such a type is successfully operating at the Clinton Engineer Works in Tennessee.

9. *Chain-reaction in natural uranium.*

As we have said before, instead of going through the lengthy process of separating U-235 isotope from the inert heavier isotope, one can try to devise some way to reduce the extinguishing effect of this heavier isotope on the neutron-chain reaction. In order to understand how it can be done, we have to learn some more details of the differences in the behavior of these two isotopes in respect to the neutrons. We have already seen that the main difference between U-235 and U-238 lies in the fact that, whereas the first nucleus, after capturing a slow neutron, breaks up into two halves, the capture of a slow neutron by the second leads simply to the formation of the heavier uranium-isotope U-239. It is also known that in respect to slow neutrons the nuclei of U-235 represent much better "catchers" than the nuclei of U-238, so that when natural uranium is bombarded by a beam of slow neutrons most of these neutrons will be caught by U-235 nuclei in spite of their rather low concentration. Thus, as soon as we have slow neutrons, the presence of the heavier uranium isotope does not present any competition to the capture-fission processes in the lighter one.

The trouble is, however, that fission-neutrons produced in the breaking-up process of U-235 are *fast* neutrons, and in respect to the fast neutrons the heavier isotope has definitely the upper hand over the lighter one. We have already mentioned the peculiar phenomenon of the resonance-capture, i.e., the abnormally increased ability of different atomic nuclei to capture incident particles with certain well defined kinetic energies. Well, the nuclei of U-238 also show this phenomenon in respect to incident neutrons, and the neutrons particularly adapted to their taste are those with the kinetic energy of about 25 micro-crocodiles. Neutrons faster or slower than that can pass near the heavy uranium nuclei without much danger, but the neutron which has the energy, say, between 24 and 26 micro-crocodiles will be swallowed for sure by the first U-238 which it encounters. Since the fast neutrons formed in the fission of one U-235 nucleus must be slowed down to the thermal energies of only 0.04 micro-crocodiles before they can affect the fission of another U-235 nucleus, they must necessarily pass through this dangerous velocity-range and thus run the risk of being swallowed by U-238 nuclei. The existence of resonance capture by a heavier isotope represents the basic reason for the impossibility of neutron chain-reactions in natural uranium, and, if we want to facilitate such a reaction without removing the heavy isotope, we must find some method of bringing the neutrons through this narrow but dangerous channel at 25 micro-crocodiles without their being inevitably swallowed by this nuclear Scylla and Charybdis. One way of doing that is by slowing down the electrons so quickly that they remain only a very short time in the dangerous velocity-range and thus do not have much chance to run into a U-238 nucleus while moving with this resonance velocity.

As we have seen before, fast neutrons can be slowed down rather quickly by letting them through some material with a small atomic weight, since in the elastic collisions with light nuclei, neutrons lose each time a considerable fraction of their kinetic energy. Such materials which slow down fast neutrons are known under the technical name of *moderators*. The fastest-working moderator is of course hydrogen, in which neutrons lose, on the average, one half of their energy in each collision. The heavier the atoms of the moderator, the smaller the energy-reduction of neutrons in each collision, and the slower the slowing-down process.

It must not be forgotten, however, that efficiency in slowing down neutrons is not the only property desired in a good moderator. In fact, the nuclei of a moderator, like all other nuclei, are able to capture the incident neutrons thus taking them out of play and cutting off the developing chain-reactions. In the case of hydrogen the capture of neutrons takes place according to the equation:

$$_1H^1 + {}_0n^1 \rightarrow {}_1D^2 + \text{radiation}$$

and is not at all a very unlikely process. Thus it may be advantageous to use as a moderator some heavier substances in which the lower rate of neutron-slowing process will be overcompensated by a smaller tendency for neutron capture.

One of such better moderators is deuterium (heavy hydrogen) in which the process of radiative capture of incident neutrons taking place according to the equation: *

$$_1D^2 + {}_0n^1 \rightarrow {}_1T^3 + \text{radiation}$$

has a considerable smaller intrinsic probability than the analogous process in ordinary hydrogen. Both hydrogen and deuterium-moderators have, however, the common disadvantage of being gases, which necessitates using them in the form of ordinary or heavy water thus introducing the additional useless atoms of oxygen. It was suggested by Fermi that the most convenient moderating-substance can be found in ordinary carbon which shows a very small tendency for neutron capture, and can be used as a pure solid substance (graphite). In the carbon moderator a fast neutron can be completely slowed down after covering the distance of about 40 centimeters. The possibility of promoting a neutron-chain-reaction in natural uranium by mixing it with a moderator and thus quickly slowing the fission neutrons to thermal velocities was first investigated by two Russian physicists, J. Zeldovich and Lewska Khariton in 1939. By using the data available at that time, they found that by mixing natural

---

* $_1T^3$—or tritium is the heavy unstable isotope of hydrogen which is transformed spontaneously into $_2He^3$ through the ejection of an electron.

uranium with ordinary water one can increase the multiplication factor only up to the value of 0.7. Since, as we have
seen above, the successful multiplication of neutron requires
more than one neutron-offspring per neutron-parent, the
expected value of only seven offsprings per ten parents is
far below the goal. This gap between what is needed and
what can be obtained was too large for cherishing any hope
that a better moderator, as for example deuterium, could
improve the situation. Thus for a while it looked as if the
only way to promote neutron-chain-reaction in natural
Uranium lay in the increase of the concentration of lighter
isotopes, which as we have seen in the previous section,
involves the extremely difficult procedures of isotope separation.

The way out of the difficulty was however soon found by
Fermi and *Szilard* who suggested that the moderator can
be made more effective if, instead of mixing it uniformly
with uranium, one uses separate uranium grains imbedded in
a large matrix of the moderating substance. In order to understand the principle of such an arrangement, which is now
generally known as *moderator-lattice*, we must remember
that fast neutrons emitted in the fission of U-235 nuclei
must fly a certain distance before they have a chance to
collide with any nucleus on their way. Thus if we have a
sufficiently small grain of natural uranium, every fission
neutron which may be formed in it will escape through the
surface before it has the chance of being captured either by
fission or by radiation-process. Suppose now that we have a
large number of such uranium grains imbedded in the continuous substance of a moderator, and located sufficiently far
from each other to secure the complete slowing down of
the neutrons emitted from one grain before they ever reach
the other (Fig. 38). With such an arrangement we can be
quite sure that *practically no fission neutrons will collide with*

*any of the uranium nuclei before they are thoroughly slowed down by passing the moderator-material.** The entire body of the moderator will be buzzing with neutrons most of them

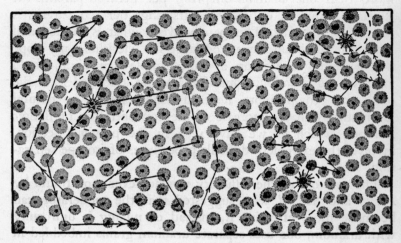

Fig. 38. A schematic presentation of neutron-chains in a pile. Smaller nuclei are those of the moderator (carbon) whereas the clusters of larger ones represent the grains of Uranium embedded in the substance of the moderator. Three neutrons ejected in the fission of Uranium 235 nucleus in one of the grains (on the left) are gradually slowed by collisions with the atoms of the moderator, and their free passing between the collisions gradually shortens. When they finally get to some other Uranium grain, their chances to produce fission are considerably improved. Two of such collisions which are likely to lead to immediate fission are shown in the picture.

already at thermal velocities, many others still in various stages of being slowed down.

A great many of the particles of this neutron-swarm will be constantly swallowed by the atomic nuclei of the moder-

---

* It is true that some fast neutrons coming from a given grain may be reflected back again by the moderator thus entering the grain with still considerable velocity, but the number of such cases will be comparatively small.

ator material, some others will manage to make their way to the surface and escape into the surrounding space, but their ranks will be continually replenished by fresh neutrons produced by those members of the swarm which re-enter the grains of uranium and cause new fission-processes. By studying the details of this picture, Fermi was able to show that by using a good moderator (carbon), and selecting the most favorable grain-sizes and distances between separate grains, it is just possible to create conditions at which the number of fresh neutrons born in uranium grains is slightly larger than the number of neutrons uselessly captured (i.e. without fission) by the nuclei of U-238 and the nuclei of carbon forming the moderator. The excess of the multiplication-factor over unity obtained in such a lattice arrangement is a very slight one, but if the birth-rate is even only slightly larger than the death-rate the population is bound to grow without any limit!

The above quoted balance between the number of neutrons which come in and out of the reaction pertains, however, only to the formation and absorption of neutrons *within* the lattice-system, and the final result will depend essentially on the additional number of neutrons coming out of the reaction by escaping through the surface into the surrounding space. If this number is small, so that neutron-production still has the edge over the combined neutron losses (i.e. inner absorption plus escape), the chain reaction will develop to the full extent. If, however, a great many neutrons have a chance to get out and away from the system, these losses will turn the balance in the opposite way. Again using the rabbit-comparison, we may say that, even when the birth-rate exceeds the death-rate, the number of rabbits in the cage will not increase if too many of them escape through a hole in the fence.

This leads us to the notion of the *critical size* of the lattice-system, a notion which has already been discussed in some detail. The critical size of the lattice system is, however, much larger than it is in the case of pure fissionable materials, since in this case too many neutrons are brought out of play by the non-fission capture *inside* the system, thus leaving a considerably smaller permissible margin for escape through the surface. (If many rabbits die from sickness within the fence, fewer can be permitted to escape, if we want the population to keep increasing!) In fact, a successfully operating lattice-system requires for its construction several tens of tons of natural uranium and several hundreds of tons of chemically pure graphite. If the lattice-system is much smaller than the critical size, a great many neutrons will escape through its surface, the reaction-chains will be cut in their very first links, and the neutron population in the system will be extremely small. If we gradually built up the lattice, bringing it closer and closer to the critical size, the density of neutron-population will become larger and the rate of energy liberation in the chain-reaction considerably increased. As soon, however, as the lattice-system becomes larger than the critical size, the situation gets out of hand, and the rapid unlimited growth of neutron-population will lead to an uncontrollable reaction which will break up the lattice.

As soon as it became clear that the lattice-arrangement can actually lead to the neutron-chain reactions in natural uranium, the construction of the first experimental lattice-system was started by Fermi, under conditions of great secrecy, at the University of Chicago. This lattice-system or pile was built from a large number of graphite bricks with a small lump of uranium imbedded in each brick. This pile was a very big pile indeed, and because of its size it was built in the spacious squash-court room under the West Stands of the Chicago's Stagg Field Stadium. The separate graphite bricks with uranium inside were laid in a regular pattern forming a giant graphite sphere, or rather an oblate spheroid flattened on the top (Fig. 39). As new layers of bricks were added, and the size of the sphere grew, the neutrons produced in its interior experienced greater and greater difficulties in getting to the surface, and the rate of nuclear reaction gradually increased. This rate was measured by counting the number of neutrons escaping through the surface and was found to increase faster and faster when the

Fig. 39. A scheme of the first Fermi-pile built from a large number of graphite blocks with a lump of natural Uranium embedded in the corners. The rods passing through the pile are made of neutron-absorbing material and serve to control the rate of the reaction.

pile was approaching the critical size. Figure 40 shows the curve representing the measured intensity of the neutron flow coming through the surface of the pile, plotted against the number of completed layers. If the pile were built beyond the critical size, indicated by an arrow in Fig. 40, the chain-reaction would get out of control and the pile would be melted and broken to pieces. To prevent this it was necessary to introduce some kind of safety-regulator and this was accomplished by using several rods made of neutron absorbing materials (cadmium or boron steel) which were inserted in slits passing all the way through the middle of the pile (Fig. 39). When these rods were all the way in,

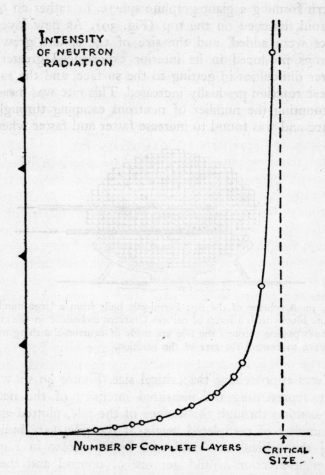

Fig. 40. A curve showing the increase of intensity in the neutron-multiplication process with the increasing number of layers of graphite blocks in the Fermi-pile. If the size of the pile should exceed the critical size indicated by an arrow, the neutron-chain reaction in the pile would get out of control.

the additional absorption of neutrons in their material turned the tables on the total neutron balance, and the chain-reaction scarcely proceeded at all. When the rods were slowly pulled out, the reaction was gradually accelerated and the pile could be brought up to its maximum efficiency. Some of these rods were connected with the apparatus measuring the intensity of the outcoming neutrons, and were automatically pushed in, thus preventing the undesired effect, as soon as the neutron-intensity approached the danger point.

An interesting point concerning these safety-regulators lies in the role played here by the delayed neutrons which were previously discussed in Section 6. In fact, if all the fission-neutrons were emitted at the moment of fission or very shortly afterwards, the increase in the rate of the chain-reaction would be almost instantaneous, and the safety regulators would not have time to move the rods into position to prevent disaster. Since, however, a certain small number of fission neutrons were emitted with a considerable delay,* and since the pile was working almost on the verge of possibility thus making every single neutron count, the development of the chain-reaction to the danger limit had to wait for these delayed neutrons, thus giving the regulating mechanism sufficient time to push in the safety rods.

The first *Fermi-pile* was completed and set into operation on December 2nd, 1942, and for the first time in human history atomic energy, hitherto hidden in the deep interior of the atom, was released by artificial means and flowed out in a well-regulated powerful stream. The rate of atomic energy generation in this first pile was brought up to about 200 watts, and could have been increased still further if it had not been prevented through consideration of possible danger to the personnel and the passersby on the streets around the

---

* 1 percent of all fission neutrons in uranium are delayed by 0.01 sec, and about 0.07 percent show a delay of a minute.

building, from the intense neutron radiation emitted by
the pile.

10. *Production of plutonium.*

We have seen in the previous section that in constructing
a giant graphite sphere with numerous small grains of natural
uranium scattered through its entire body, it is possible to
out-balance the expected neutron losses by neutron production in the grains, thus establishing the conditions for the
development of neutron-chain-reaction, and the large scale
liberation of the hidden energy of U-235 nuclei. Although
the construction of the Fermi-pile represents one of the
greatest scientific achievements, it can hardly be used directly
as a convenient practical source of atomic energy. In fact, as
already discussed above, the main advantage of atomic energy
sources lies in their compactness which permits us to obtain
large amounts of energy from a very small amount of
material.

The Fermi-pile, with the immense amount of graphite and
uranium in its construction, must be considered to be
anything but a compact energy source. Furthermore, as is
known to any engineer, the heat energy liberated by any
kind of source can be used successfully for the production of
mechanical work only if this heat originates at very high
temperatures, and the operation of the Fermi-pile at the temperatures above a few hundred degrees presents immense
difficulties. Of course one can put such a pile in one's basement (if one has a basement large enough!), and use it for
heating the house, but it will be about as expensive as throw-
ing into your furnace shovelfuls of diamonds which, as
everybody knows, are actually made of carbon and with a
good draft will burn almost as satisfactorily as ordinary coal.
Of course nobody ever had the crazy idea of dropping the
Fermi-pile on an enemy city; that would have achieved

nothing beyond possibly crushing the skulls of a few of the inhabitants.

Apart from its purely scientific interest, the great value of the Fermi-pile lies in one of the side products of the nuclear-chain-reaction which takes place in its interior. We have already seen that the pile is working just on the verge of possibility, and that from two or three neutrons produced by each fission-process in its interior, only slightly more than one (on the average) has the chance of producing a subsequent fission thus supporting the process of the chain-reaction. Other neutrons produced in the fission processes will partially escape through the surface of the pile, but will mostly be captured by atomic nuclei of the moderator material and those of the heavier uranium isotope in the grains. The capture of these surplus neutrons by carbon nuclei leads to the formation of the stable carbon isotope with the atomic weight 13 which is of no special interest. But when a neutron is captured by the heavy uranium isotope, thus forming a still heavier isotope U-239, something very interesting happens.

This nucleus is intrinsically unstable, having too many neutrons, and is therefore subject to an internal electric rearrangement in which two neutrons are turned into protons, and two negative electrons are ejected one after another. The first electron takes on the average 23 minutes to get out; the second comes 2 days and 8 hours later. The ejection of these negative electrons changes the atomic number of the nucleus from the original value 92 to 93 and then to 94. Thus we obtain the atoms of two new chemical elements located beyond uranium in the periodic system, and not existing normally in nature. These two transuranium elements, the existence of which had been suspected by Fermi in 1935, are now known under the names of *neptunium* and *plutonium*. The names are quite appropriate, considering that

Neptune and Pluto are the next two planets located beyond Uranus in our solar system, but it puts the physicists in a rather inconvenient position of having to wait for further progress in the discovery of new planets before coming to the study of elements with atomic number 95, 96, etc. And there is no doubt that there are at least a few such elements beyond plutonium. The alchemical equation of the nuclear processes involved in the formation of plutonium from the heavy uranium-isotope subjected to neutron-bombardment can be written in the form:

$$_{92}U^{238} + _{0}n^1 \rightarrow _{92}U^{239} + \text{radiation}$$
$$_{92}U^{239} \rightarrow _{93}Np^{239} + \text{negative electron}$$
$$_{93}Np^{239} \rightarrow _{94}Pu^{239} + \text{negative electron}$$

The new element plutonium is similar to uranium or thorium in its radioactive properties, and is a long-lived element with a decay-period of a few tens of thousands of years, which, by emission of an alpha-particle, turns into actino-uranium which is the same as U-235. We have already discussed this question in Section 4, where we have also stated that plutonium, as probably are all transuranium elements, is easily fisssionable so that its nuclei can be broken up by slow neutrons. Thus, *while the progressing neutron-chain-reaction in the Fermi-pile is slowly destroying the nuclei of lighter uranium isotope by breaking them in two and liberating their hidden energy, it also builds up the nuclei of heavy uranium isotope into still heavier nuclei of plutonium.* Of course, plutonium produced in such a process, being itself an easily fissionable element, will be in its turn gradually destroyed by the neutron-swarm so that its total amount in the material of the pile can never become too large. When the chain-reaction in the pile loaded with fresh uranium has just started, the concentration of plutonium will gradually increase from zero to a certain maximum value at which the rate of its destruction becomes equal to the rate of its production from U-235. Beyond this point the content-ratio of plutonium to U-235 will remain constant and the total amount of plutonium will begin to decrease along with the gradual exhaustion of U-235 in the original material (Fig. 41). This is the moment when we have to stop the reaction if we want to obtain the maximum possible amount of plutonium in our sample.

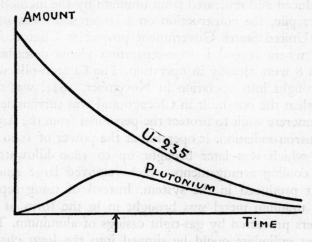

Fig. 41. Time-changes in the amount of U-235 and Plutonium as the process in the pile is going on. Plutonium must be separated when its concentration reaches the maximum at the moment indicated by an arrow.

But what is the good of building plutonium at the expense of the destroyed U-235 if both the substances seem to be about equally efficient in the fission phenomenon produced by slow neutrons? Well, plenty! The point is that *plutonium formed this way in the uranium-material can be much more easily separated from it, since having atomic number 94 it is a different element possessing different chemical properties from uranium.* Thus we do not need to go through all the complicated and slow methods of isotope-separation needed in the case of U-235, and can get plutonium from the uranium in which it is formed by the classical methods of analytic chemistry. Not quite classical, though, since the chemical properties of plutonium are not to be found in any existing textbook of chemistry, and the chemistry of this new element had to be worked out completely anew.

When it was shown beyond any doubt that plutonium can be produced and separated from uranium by the method of a graphite pile, the construction on a larger scale was started at the United States Government project at Clinton, Tennessee, where several isotope-separation plants described in Section 8 were already in operation. The Clinton-pile which was brought into operation in November, 1943, was much larger than the one built in Chicago and was surrounded by solid concrete walls to protect the personnel from the dangerous neutron-radiation. It operated at the power of 1000 kilowatts, which was later brought up to 1800 kilowatts by better cooling arrangements which removed large amounts of heat produced in the system. Instead of using separate grains, uranium metal was brought in in the form of long cylinders protected by gas-tight casings of aluminum. These uranium cylinders could be slipped into the long channels running through the graphite body of the pile, and then could be easily removed when the necessary amount of plutonium was cooked. The vigorous cooling system kept the temperature of these uranium cylinders at only 150°C, and the entire system was operated by remote control from behind thick walls. By March 1944, the pile delivered several grams of pure plutonium, and the production was going on at full speed.

Although making several grams of an element which does not exist anywhere in the Universe can be considered as quite an achievement on the part of practical alchemy, the rate of production of a single Clinton-pile was far from enough to produce in a comparatively short time the kilograms of plutonium which were needed for the construction of atomic bombs. Thus under the pressure of war, a new and much larger plutonium production plant was built by the United States Government in the State of Washington on the shores of the Columbia river, the cold waters of which were very useful for cooling the giant graphite piles in which the plutonium was cooked. It may be remarked here that the cooling problem is very important when plutonium is being produced on a large scale. For example, a plant producing one kilogram of plutonium per day must operate at a power of one million kilowatts, liberating enough heat to bring to boiling point 150 tons of ice-cold water every minute. This giant enterprise, known as *Hanford Plant*, started in June 1943, and was in full operation by the summer of 1945. It covers an area of nearly one thousand square miles, in which are located numerous laboratories, work-shops, and chemical separation plants, all subordinated to the three giant piles cooking plutonium day and night and heating the Columbia River by the streams of hot water coming out of their cooling systems.

The materials produced on this giant alchemical plant, as well as those coming from Clinton, are being carefully stored in neutron-tight containers, and are undoubtedly destined to play much more important roles in the future economic and political position of this country than all the gold resting in the underground vaults of Fort Knox!

11. *Atomic explosions.*

Now that we know how to produce in sufficient quantities such fissionable elements as U-235 or plutonium, the next question is how this highly concentrated energy can be used. There are, of course, two different ways to utilize the atomic energy which the progress of science has put into our hands.

We can either release it instantaneously in the form of a violent explosion, destroying everything for miles around, or we can let it flow out in a steady stream to supply power to various kinds of machinery. Since the discovery of uranium-fission coincided with the beginning of the greatest war in the entire history of the human race, it was only natural that the main interest of the people working on that problem was directed towards the first objective: the atomic bomb. Provided we have a sufficient amount of U-235, plutonium, or some other fissionable transuranium element, how can we make it explode? Well, it does not seem to be so difficult, and probably a more reasonable form of the question would be: how can we keep these materials from exploding?

We have seen in the discussions of this chapter that neutron-chain-reaction in fissionable materials is in principle a self-accelerating, or explosive, reaction, being much more similar to the chemical reactions in nitroglycerine or TNT than to those taking place in the burning of coal or oil. We have seen that in order to prevent these chain-reactions from developing into an explosion, one has to use such small samples of fissionable materials that most of the neutrons formed in their interiors escape through the surface, thus coming out of play. It follows that *all we have to do in order to produce an atomic explosion is to take several pieces of fissionable material, each one smaller than critical size, and bring them rapidly together, thus forming one large lump.*

The only question is, how fast must the separate pieces be brought together? To answer this question we have first to understand a little better what the word "explosion" exactly means.

When the safety valve of a steam-boiler is jammed, and the pressure continues to rise, there comes a moment when the steel walls cannot hold any more and break up, letting out the hot steam. Although such a phenomenon would be commonly named "the explosion of a steam boiler," it is not an explosion as this word should be used in a strictly scientific sense. In fact, the power of such a pseudo-explosion depends not so much on the properties of the steam as on the strength of the boiler's walls. If the walls are very thin and break up easily, the "explosion" of the boiler will take place under quite small pressure; if the walls are stronger the pressure of the "explosion" will be higher but under no circumstances can the "explosion" of a steam boiler develop pressure higher than the tensile strength of steel.

On the other hand, in the explosion of a bomb loaded with some ordinary military explosive the metal walls play a very unimportant role, serving only as a container which holds the charge. They are torn apart as easily as thin cardboard when the explosion takes place. The presence of walls is quite unessential to the process of explosion, and, in fact, a piece of TNT can be exploded just as well without any container. Why then does the explosion of TNT develop such terrific pressure which tears holes in thick armor-plates and pushes down the walls of big buildings? The explanation lies in the fact that the transformation of chemical explosives into a hot gas takes place so fast that the material *does not have enough time to expand* before the reaction is completed. We deal here with the forces of inertia in the explosive material itself which prevent it from flying instantaneously apart, and thus cause the delay of the expansion which is necessary for the development of high pressure. These are the same forces of inertia which prevent a door from swinging open when a bullet is shot into it. The energy of the bullet, which is in itself quite sufficient to turn the door on its hinges, is applied so fast that *the door does not have time to move,* and the pressure developed in the point where the bullet hits tears a hole in the wood.

When a charge of ordinary chemical explosive goes off, its material turns into hot gases so fast that, even in the absence of confining walls, these gases occupy the original volume of the charge. This results in a very high local pressure which is responsible for the highly destructive effect of an explosion.

If, on the contrary, the reaction takes place more slowly, so that the expansion starts while the transformation is still in progress, the pressure will never have the chance to be built up to maximum possible value and we will have a long *pushing effect* instead of instantaneous shock. This is, for example, the case in the "explosion" of the gasoline-air mixture in the cylinders of an automobile motor where the reaction is going on all the time while the piston is moving back. If, in fact, the same mixture could be made to release all its energy instantaneously, the cylinders would certainly crack and be broken into many pieces.

It is easy to estimate how quickly the transformation of a metastable substance must actually take place to result in a true explosion. In order to do this we have to find out how fast the reacting material can propel itself at the expense of the energy liberated in its own internal transformation. It will be remembered from the discussions of the first chapter that ordinary chemical reactions liberate about 1000 calories per gram of the material. In the units of mechanical energy this is equivalent to 4.10^{10} ergs.* Since the kinetic energy per unit mass of a moving material is determined by one half of the square of its velocity, we find that the energy liberated in chemical transformation can propel this material with the speed of about $2.5 . 10^5$ centimeters or two and a half kilometers per second. The actual value will be somewhat smaller since part of the energy liberated in the transformation re-

* As we have said before, one calory is equivalent to 4.10^7 ergs of mechanical energy.

mains in the form of heat and does not go into the energy of motion, so that when an explosion takes place the resulting hot gases are propelled outwards at the speed of about a kilometer per second. Therefore, in order that the transformation be completed before a considerable expansion of the charge, say by one centimeter, takes place, it is necessary that the reaction time be shorter than one hundred thousandth of a second. And, in fact, in all good chemical explosives the complete transformation of metastable molecules require only few microseconds (one millionth of a second) to be completed.

As we have seen before, atomic transformations liberate twenty million times more energy per gram than ordinary chemical reactions, from which it follows that the velocity with which an exploding atomic charge would expand is about five thousand times (i.e. the square root of twenty millions) larger than that in the case of ordinary chemical explosives. *Thus if the atomic explosion is to take place at almost constant volume, the reaction must be completed several thousand times faster: not in a few millionths but rather a thousand millionth part of a second (a millimicrosecond).*

Unfortunately the neutron-chain reactions in fissionable material do not seem to be able to take place so quickly. In fact, as we have seen before, the complete development of the chain requires at least 50 consecutive branching links, each separate link involving a fission-capture of a fast neutron emitted in the previous fission. Since the distance to be covered by a fast neutron, going at the speed of about ten thousand kilometers per second,* before it has the chance to produce another fission, is about ten centimeters, the time-interval corresponding to one link is about one hundred millionth part of a second. Fifty consecutive links, necessary for

* This velocity corresponds to a neutron with the energy of one crocodile.

the completion of nuclear reaction, will take fifty times longer or altogether about half a microsecond, i.e. not much shorter than in the case of chemical explosions. The above numbers represent, of course, only a very rough estimate, but they show rather definitely that *the time necessary for the development of the neutron-chain reaction in fissionable material is considerably longer than the time-interval necessary for this material to fly apart under the action of developing pressure.*

This does not mean, of course, that atomic explosions based on neutron-chain-reactions are impossible, but only that, instead of being true explosions producing an instantaneous shock, they are of a more continuous nature still developing energy while the expansion of the original material is already in progress. An ordinary chemical material reacting in such a way would be not considered as a good explosive at all, but it must not be forgotten that atomic explosives have the edge over ordinary explosives by being twenty million times more powerful. And, having a factor of twenty millions in power, one should not worry much about losing even quite a bit in the performance!

Now we return to our question about how fast separate small pieces of fissionable materials have to be brought together to result in an explosion. It is clear that it must be done faster than the explosion itself takes place, since otherwise the reaction beginning while the two pieces approach each other will throw them apart before they actually come into contact. Thus, for example, if we have two liquids which explode when mixed together, and do not mix them up sufficiently fast, a small partial explosion will take place when the first few drops come into contact, spilling the rest of the liquid uselessly around. If a nuclear-chain-reaction took place in one millimicro-second which is necessary for a true atomic explosion, we would face the almost impossible task of bringing the pieces together in that extremely short interval of time. But the comparative slowness of nuclear reaction, which makes it not a true explosion, facilitates the problem of "assembling the bomb," as the process of bringing together the pieces is technically called, to quite a large extent. In fact, to bring together the pieces which were originally at a distance of, say, several centimeters within the time interval of a few microseconds requires the velocity of only several kilometers per second, which is not much in excess of ordinary bullet-velocities. *Thus in order to produce an atomic explosion one must shoot one piece of fissionable material into another with the speed of a fast bullet.*

How it is exactly done, and how the atomic bomb is actually constructed is, of course, a closely guarded military secret, but the author does not see any reason why he should not tell it to his readers who may be interested in constructing one of such atomic bombs of their own. It is, in fact, very easy and reminds the author of an incident which happened many years ago when he once went with a couple of friends to see a famous magician. The magician was performing the most unbelievable things, taking rabbits out of his hat, piercing himself with long steel swords, and catching lighted cigarettes out of thin air. When all the demonstration was finished and the audience was sitting with wide open eyes and holding their breaths, the magician said that now he would be very glad to explain all his tricks so that everybody in the audience could perform them for their friends and relatives. While he was speaking, the orchestra, which had been playing soft music all during the performance, went crescendo, playing louder and louder. And before one could catch the first words of explanation, the brass was roaring, the big drum was sounding like a field-howitzer, and the assembled violins were screeching louder than a hundred cats pulled by their tails. One could see the mouth of the magician moving but not a single word was heard. The auditorium did not apparently include deaf people who could read lips, but even if such were present they would not get the secret since the magician was most probably quoting some poetry which he knew by heart. After five or ten minutes of such explanation, the orchestra which by that time came to the top of its performance suddenly became silent, and with a bow the magician expressed the hope that his explanation was understood by everybody and would help them to perform the same tricks. So let us hope that the reader now understands how to construct an atomic bomb for the benefit of his friends and relatives.

The construction of an atomic bomb, according to the above described simple principle, is however not at all an easy task. The main point is that due to the scarcity of fissionable material and to the comparatively large amounts of these material needed for each single explosion, one could not proceed in the way of ordinary military practice in which dozens of bombs of new construction are dropped just to see how their fuses are functioning. Thus, one had to work precisely, which meant calculating in advance every single detail of the nuclear chain-reaction involved, the sizes and the shapes of separate pieces used, and all the phenomena expected to take place in the process of the "assembly" which had to lead to the explosion. This giant task was undertaken under the general leadership of *J. R. Oppenheimer*, theoretical physicist from the University of California, in the third secret atomic bomb site at Los Almos near Santa Fe, New Mexico. The work carried out here included both detailed experimental study of various processes participating in neutron-chain reactions, as well as the advance-calculations of the functioning of the bomb. As everybody knows, this work resulted in the first, experimental atomic bomb which was exploded in the New Mexican desert on the

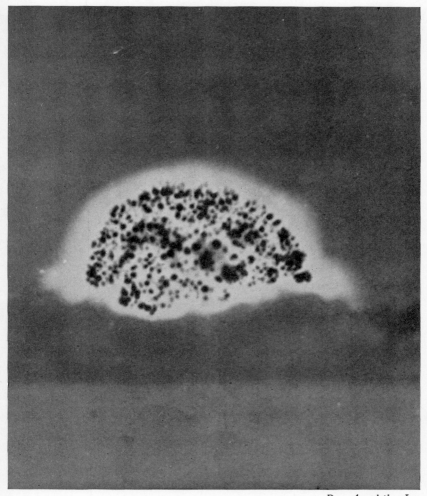

Press Association, Inc.

PLATE IV.

A picture showing the fragments of original charge flying through the glare with nuclear reaction probably still going in their interiors. The fragments are extremely luminous and appear black only because of the inversion of the photographic plate under the action of too high light-intensity.

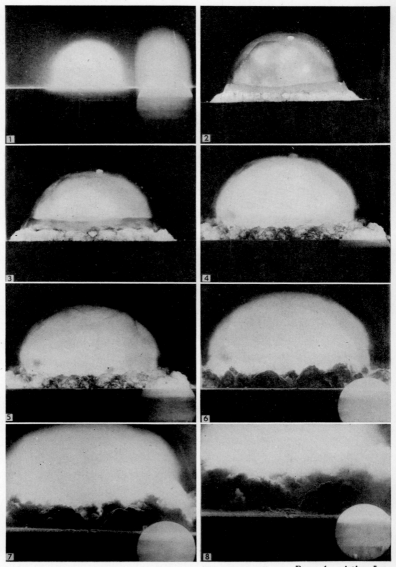

Press Association, Inc.

PLATE V.

Eight consecutive stages of the development of the atomic explosion in the New Mexican desert.

morning of July 16th, 1945, and verified in all details the expectations of its constructors.

In Plates IV and V are reproduced several photographs representing various stages of the explosion. Although the detailed descriptions of all phenomena which took place at the explosion of the atomic bomb are at present not available, it may be suggested that the black spots on the first photograph are in reality very luminous, and appear black in the picture only because the radiation was so intense that it "burned holes" in the photographic emulsion on the negative. They are probably fragments of the original charge flying apart while the nuclear reactions may still be going on in their interior. The strongly illuminated region around the explosion is probably the effect of illumination or the glare of the surrounding atmosphere, caused by intensely strong gamma-radiation emitted in the process of nuclear chain reaction. Owing to its terrific intensity, gamma-radiation emitted by the exploding bomb strips off the electrons from practically every single atom within a certain radius. Jumping back to their original positions in the atoms, these electrons emit a large amount of ultraviolet and visible light, which is responsible for the high luminosity of the phenomenon. We have here something like a miniature model of the sun where the atomic energy released by nuclear reactions near the center is traveling towards the surface through a number of successive absorption- and reemition-processes, changing gradually from the high-frequency gamma-radiation into the visible light escaping from the surface. The difference lies, of course, in the fact that, whereas in the case of the sun we have a continuously alchemic reaction securing the permanently high temperature of the solar surface, the explosion of the atomic bomb gives us only an instantaneous energy-release so that the phenomenon of the luminous sphere lasts only for a fraction of a second. The surface temperature developed in the atomic explosion must be at least equal to and is probably higher than, the temperature of the sun, so that, for a short time while it lasts, any object or person exposed to its radiation within a short distance is in the position of being the same distance from the surface of the sun itself. And nobody will doubt that *it is not a very pleasant experience to come even for a short time so close to the surface of the sun!*

Thus, apart from the blast-wave caused by the "atomic explosion," the destructive effects of which are probably smaller than they would have been if it were a true explosion in the above described sense, we have here a terrific burning power which was amply verified by the two atomic bombs dropped on the Japanese cities. We will not enter here in the discussion of the unpleasant effects of the radiation of the atomic bomb on the persons exposed to it at sufficiently large distances not to be burned alive, nor will we speak about the possible poisoning effects by the long-lived radioactive elements produced in such explosions. This is a book on physics and not on the science of medicine teaching how to cure human beings, or on military science teaching how to destroy them. And, in any case, all these effects cannot be discussed in detail before thorough investigations are carried out.

It may be added though, that it is a pity from the point of view of pure knowledge (or curiosity?) that after the first atomic bomb demonstrated its destructive effect on a Japanese city, the second one was not used in some other way. Should it have been dropped, for example, in the waters of an important naval base where enemy warships were anchored, one probably could have observed a giant wave depositing large battleships on the roofs of the harbor installations and surrounding buildings (Fig. 42). But, this may be demonstrated in the future.

Fig. 42. Two military applications of the atomic bomb. *a.* The bomb explodes at a certain height above the city, setting it afire by intensive radiation, and producing additional destruction by a high-pressure blastwave. *b.* Underwater explosion of an atomic bomb. A terrific wave produced by high pressure at the place of explosion plays havoc with the enemy fleet.

12. *Peaceful uses of atomic power.*

As already stated many times before, the atomic energy of uranium is not a cheap energy, partly because uranium itself is a rather rare element, partly because of the complexity of the process of isotope-separation or plutonium production. At this early stage of the new industry it is very difficult to say what the final cost of uranium energy will be, but it does not seem likely that even the commercially more promising method of plutonium-production in graphite piles will be able to bring the cost of uranium-energy below that of ordinary coal. But the advantage of the uranium or plutonium energy sources lies not in their possible cheapness, but in the high degree of energy concentration in a given amount of material. Thus they are bound to play a very important role in all cases where such highly concentrated fuels are needed, most probably in the construction of jet-propelled

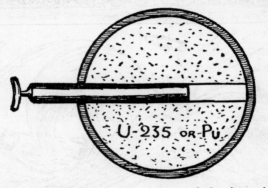

Fig. 43. A simplified picture of an atomic heating unit.

airplanes for long distance flights, and particularly in the construction of many different kinds of rockets.

The most direct method of using the energy of neutronchain-reaction in fissionable materials, consists, of course, in taking a lump of these materials just below the critical size and regulating the rate of the energy-liberating reaction by an energy-absorbing rod which can be slipped into a channel running through the material (Fig. 43). This is, of course, the same arrangement as in the Fermi graphite piles, with the exception that pure fissionable materials are to be used. The heat developed by the nuclear chain reactions in this regulated atomic heating unit can be then transformed into mechanical work by one of the ordinary engineering methods. One can use it, for example, for raising steam in various types of steam engines, or for heating the air to be then expelled under high pressure through the driving valves of jet-propelled planes or rockets.

However, the direct use of fissionable materials in motors has three serious disadvantages. One of these disadvantages lies in the large amount of fissionable material which would be needed for one single heating unit. In fact, the unit will operate only if it is about the critical size, which means many kilograms of U-235 or plutonium. The second, closely connected, disadvantage is of course the danger of explosion, since the load of such a heating unit will be about the same as one puts into the atomic bomb. The third, and probably the most serious disadvantage lies in the intensive gamma-ray and neutron-emission which will come from such an atomic motor while it is functioning. The pilots and passengers of the plane driven by plutonium-power would have to be protected against this radiation by thick walls of solid lead weighing many tons. This is, of course, not very practicable for any small size vehicle, and especially for aircraft!

It is not, however, at all necessary to put the fissionable elements themselves into the motors of planes, automobiles, or any other kind of vehicle, since we can accumulate the uranium energy produced in large central plants *in some kind of special "atomic storage batteries" which do not possess any of the above three disadvantages*. In fact, by subjecting the ordinary stable elements to the intensive neutron-radiation produced in uranium piles, we can transform them into various radioactive elements in the very same way as U-238 is transformed into U-239, which later decays into plutonium. The radioactive elements produced in this way will provide a constant source of heat to be used in the power-generators, and will be completely free from the possibility of atomic explosion. If we select, from the large variety of such elements, those which have a suitable decay period and also do not possess specifically strong gamma-radiation, we can produce heating units adaptable for every purpose. The main advantage of such atomic storage batteries lies in the fact that they can be used in any desirable amount: in large quantities for big transatlantic airliners, or in small quantities for model airplanes of our airminded young generation.

The only serious disadvantage of these atomic-storage-batteries is that they cannot be stopped and continue to produce energy in a steady flow from the very first moment they are "charged" at the atomic power plant. But, of course, we have to pay this price if we do not want to use neutron-chain-reactions which are at present the only nuclear reactions the speed of which can be regulated at will. The reader will remember that, as discussed in the second chapter of this book, the best controllable nuclear reactions are those involving the thermo-nuclear transformation of various elements, but that the use of such sources is extremely difficult, and very likely will never be realized, because of the extremely high temperatures required.

Thus, it seems that at the present time our best bet for using atomic energy for practical purposes lies in producing it from natural uranium at giant central power plants, in delivering it to the places where it is needed in atomic storage-batteries made of radioactive elements or some artificial electron-emitters.

Though the high cost of this energy and the constant leakage of atomic-storage batteries, will probably never make it practicable to put such motors in passenger cars which spend most of their time parked on the street or standing in the garage, it will certainly be used very soon in all cases where a constant supply of high power is needed regardless of cost.

Probably one of the most exciting applications of atomic power to which we can look forward is the possibility of constructing a rocket ship which defies the forces of gravity and flies out into space for a visit to the moon or to the planets of our solar system. The main difficulty of all previous projects of intraplanetary communication lay in the fact that all ordinary chemical fuels have too small a concentration of energy. In order to fly out of the Earth's gravitational field, a rocket ship, like any other object, must acquire the speed of over eleven kilometers per second, which is known as *escape velocity*. In order to understand why the ordinary chemical fuels which could be used in the motor of such a rocket ship could not possibly give it the necessary velocity we have first to be acquainted a little with the principles of rocket-flying in empty space.

A rocket flies ahead because the gases ejected from its rear give it a recoil similar to that observed in the rifle or a gun shooting out a fast projectile. According to the laws of mechanics the velocities of the gun-recoil and the projectile stand in the inverse ratio to their masses. Thus the recoil-velocities of rifles and guns are so much smaller than the velocities of the projectiles they shoot, because they are so much heavier than the projectiles. A rocket flying through empty space * will acquire a velocity which is as many times smaller than the velocity of jet-gases, as the mass of the rocket itself is larger than the total mass of ejected gases (Fig. 44).

We have seen in the general discussion of explosions in the previous section that the chemical energy stored in metastable materials is enough only to propel them at the speed of a few kilometers per second. Thus if a rocket ship ejecting

---

* In flight through the air, as in the case of jet-propelled planes, the situation is much more complicated because of the friction against the air preventing the acceleration of the aircraft, and the fact that jet-gases coming out of the muzzle encounter the inert air masses which help to increase the push.

the gases with that speed from its rear values is to acquire the speed of over 11 kilometers per second necessary to escape from the Earth, the total mass of the ejected material must exceed the mass of the rocket itself by a factor of about ten. Since in traveling through empty space the rocket-ship has to carry with itself everything which has to be thrown out, the fuel load must form more than 90 percent of the total weight of the ship at the start. More detailed estimates lead to an even less favorable percentage. And from a purely constructional point of view it becomes extremely difficult,

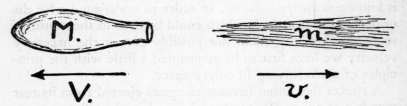

Fig. 44. The principle of rocket-propulsion. The finite velocity of the rocket (V.) and the velocity of the expelled material (v.) stand in inverse proportion to their masses (M. and m.).

if not impossible, to build such a light rocket body which would carry such a heavy fuel load.

If, instead of using chemical energy we use atomic energy, the velocity of self-propulsion of reacting materials increases by a factor of several thousands, which reduces the minimum amount of fuel in space-rocket from over 90 percent of the total weight to less than one percent. Thus a rocket-ship weighing say ten tons, can fly out into intraplanetary space using only about 100 pounds of fuel, an amount comparable to that used in one atomic bomb.

The situation is, however, far from being as simple as it may look at first glance, and although we have now a sufficiently condensed energy source, and the total fuel-load needed for the trip can be carried aboard ship by one crewmember, we still face the tremendous technical problem of using this energy for producing a powerful jet escaping from the driving-valves with the needed high speed.

A normal procedure for obtaining such jets would consist in using the heat developed by atomic fuel (plutonium, or atomic storage-batteries) for vaporizing some "driving-fluid" carried along in the rocket, and letting the hot gases out under very high pressure through small openings in the rear of the ship. However, in order to have the high velocities necessary for propulsion, the gases must go out under ex-

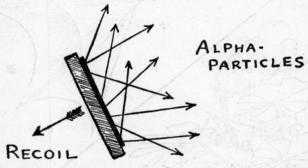

Fig. 45. Alpha-particles emitted from a thin layer of a radioactive substance deposited on a plate, set the plate in motion.

tremely high pressure which raises the question about the strength of the chamber walls, etc.

It may be suggested that, instead of turning the kinetic energy of high-speed particles originating in nuclear reactions into heat and then converting this heat again into the kinetic energy of gas flow, one could use directly the mechanical recoil of reacting nuclei. Thus, for example, if we have a thin layer of alpha-decaying radioactive substance spread on a supporting metal plate, alpha-particles ejected from decaying atomic nuclei will give to the plate a recoil-push in the opposite direction and make it move with steadily increasing

velocity (Fig. 45). The layer must be rather thin (a fraction
of a millimeter) to prevent the alpha-particles formed in its
interior from being stuck in it before they reach the surface.
The necessary thinness of the layer, and a rather large amount
of radioactive material necessary to drive the rocket-ship,

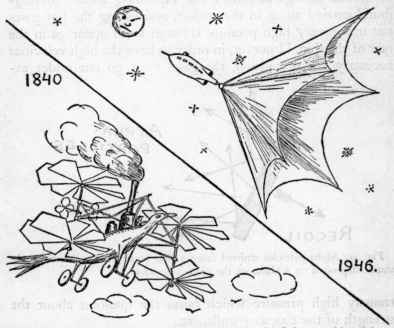

Fig. 46. Two crazy ideas a century apart. An old flying machine driven
by a steam-engine, and the new project of a rocketship using a sail. Actual
rockets of the future may be expected to look quite different!

would require a very large area emitting alpha-particles, so
that the whole thing will look like a giant sail with the area
of probably many hundred square feet. An arrangement of
this kind could be imagined in the way presented in Fig. 46.
A thin metal-sheet forming the sail, and covered on one side
with a deposit of radioactive material emitting alpha-particles,

might be folded as an umbrella while the rocket-ship is crossing the thick layers of terrestrial atmosphere being driven in the initial stages of its journey by an ordinary chemical jet-propulsion motor. When it gets out into the empty interstellar space it opens its tail and sails proud as a peacock towards the stars. We give the idea here for what it is worth, although it is quite certain that the space ships of the future will resemble this "peacock-model" just as little as the modern B-29 resembles the curious flying machine as it presented itself to the eyes of the people of the nineteenth century.

Let us hope that the best important achievement of atomic energy will lie in planetary exploration, and not in human destruction.

NUCLEAR SPECIES

This table includes all nuclei with a balanced number of neutrons and protons. The main (most abundant) isotopes of each element are given in heavy type. The isotopes unstable in respect to alpha-decay are given in brackets.

Atomic Number	Chemical Symbol	Full Name	Masses of Isotopes (Nearest Integer)
1	H	Hydrogen	1, 2
2	He	Helium	3, 4
3	Li	Lithium	6, 7
4	Be	Beryllium	9
5	B	Boron	10, 11
6	C	Carbon	12, 13
7	N	Nitrogen	14, 15
8	O	Oxygen	16, 17, 18
9	F	Fluorine	19
10	Ne	Neon	20, 21, 22
11	Na	Sodium	23
12	Mg	Magnesium	24, 25, 26
13	Al	Aluminum	27
14	Si	Silicon	28, 29, 30
15	P	Phosphorus	31
16	S	Sulphur	32, 33, 34
17	Cl	Chlorine	35, 37
18	A	Argon	36, 38, 40
19	K	Potassium	39, 41
20	Ca	Calcium	40, 42, 43, 44
21	Sc	Scandium	45
22	Ti	Titanium	46, 47, 48, 49, 50
23	V	Vanadium	51
24	Cr	Chromium	50, 52, 53, 54
25	Mn	Manganese	55
26	Fe	Iron	54, 56, 57, 58
27	Co	Cobalt	57, 59
28	Ni	Nickel	58, 60, 61, 62, 64
29	Cu	Copper	63, 65
30	Zn	Zinc	64, 66, 67, 68, 70
31	Ga	Gallium	69, 71
32	Ge	Germanium	70, 72, 73, 74, 76
33	As	Arsenic	75
34	Se	Selenium	74, 76, 77, 78, 80, 82
35	Br	Bromine	79, 81
36	Kr	Krypton	78, 80, 82, 83, 84, 86
37	Rb	Rubidium	85, 87
38	Sr	Strontium	84, 86, 87, 88
39	Y	Yttrium	89
40	Zr	Zirconium	90, 91, 92, 94, 96
41	Nb	Niobium	93
42	Mo	Molybdenum	92, 94, 95, 96, 97, 98, 100
43	Ms	Masurium	β-decaying isotopes only
44	Ru	Ruttenium	96, 98, 99, 100, 101, 102,, 104
45	Rh	Rhodium	101, 103
46	Pd	Palladium	102, 104, 105, 106, 108, 110
47	Ag	Silver	107, 109
48	Cd	Cadmium	106, 108, 110, 111, 112, 113, 114, 116
49	In	Indium	113, 115
50	Sn	Tin	112, 114, 115, 116, 117, 118, 119, 120, 122, 124

Atomic Number	Chemical Symbol	Full Name	Masses of Isotopes (Nearest Integer)
51	Sb	Antimony	121, 123
52	Te	Tellurium	120, 122, 123, 124, 125, 126, 128, 130
53	I	Iodine	127
54	Xe	Xenon	124, 126, 128, 129, 130, 131, 132, 134, 136
55	Cs	Caesium	133
56	Ba	Barium	130, 132, 134, 135, 136, 137, 138
57	La	Lanthanum	139
58	Ce	Cerium	136, 138, 140, 142
59	Pr	Praseodymium	141
60	Nd	Neodymium	142, 143, 144, 145, 146, 148, 150
61	Il	Illinium	β-decaying isotopes only
62	Sm	Samarium	144, 147, 148, 149, 150, 152, 154
63	Eu	Europium	151, 153
64	Gd	Gadolinium	155, 156, 157, 158, 160
65	Tb	Terbium	159
66	Dy	Dysprosium	161, 162, 163, 164
67	Ho	Holmium	165
68	Er	Erbium	166, 167, 168, 170
69	Tm	Thulium	169
70	Yb	Ytterbium	171, 172, 173, 174, 176
71	Lu	Lutecium	175
72	Hf	Hafnium	176, 177, 178, 179, 180
73	Ta	Tantalum	181
74	W	Tungsten	182, 183, 184, 186
75	Re	Rhenium	185, 187
76	Os	Osmium	186, 187, 188, 189, 190, 192
77	Ir	Iridium	191, 193
78	Pt	Platinum	192, 194, 195, 196, 198
79	Au	Gold	197
80	Hg	Mercury	196, 198, 199, 200, 201, 202, 204
81	Tl	Thallium	203, 205
82	Pb	Lead	204, 206, 207, 208
83	Bi	Bismuth	209
84	Po	Polonium	[210] [211] [212] [214] [215] [216] [218]
85	Ab	Alabamium	β-decaying isotopes only
86	Rn	Radon	[219] [220] [222]
87	Vi	Virginium	β-decaying isotopes only
88	Ra	Radium	[223] [224] [226]
89	Ac	Actinium	β-decaying isotopes only
90	Th	Thorium	[230] [232]
91	Pa	Protactinium	[231]
92	U	Uranium	[234] [235] [238]
93	Np	Neptunium	β-decaying isotopes only
94	Pu	Plutonium	[238] [239]

Atomic Number	Chemical Symbol	Full Name	Masses of Isotopes (Normal Italicized)
51	Sb	Antimony	121, 123
52	Te	Tellurium	120, 122, 123, 124, 125, 126, 128, 130
53	I	Iodine	127
54	Xe	Xenon	124, 126, 128, 129, 130, 131, 132, 134, 136
55	Cs	Caesium	133
56	Ba	Barium	130, 132, 134, 135, 136, 137, 138
57	La	Lanthanum	139
58	Ce	Cerium	136, 138, 140, 142
59	Pr	Praseodymium	141
60	Nd	Neodymium	142, 143, 144, 145, 146, 148, 150
61	Il	Illinium	(decaying isotopes only)
62	Sm	Samarium	144, 147, 148, 149, 150, 152, 154
63	Eu	Europium	151, 153
64	Gd	Gadolinium	152, 154, 155, 156, 157, 158, 160
65	Tb	Terbium	159
66	Dy	Dysprosium	156, 158, 160, 161, 162, 163, 164
67	Ho	Holmium	165
68	Er	Erbium	162, 164, 166, 167, 168, 170
69	Tm	Thulium	169
70	Yb	Ytterbium	168, 170, 171, 172, 173, 174, 176
71	Lu	Lutecium	175
72	Hf	Hafnium	174, 176, 177, 178, 179, 180
73	Ta	Tantalum	181
74	W	Tungsten	182, 183, 184, 186
75	Re	Rhenium	185, 187
76	Os	Osmium	186, 187, 188, 189, 190, 192
77	Ir	Iridium	191, 193
78	Pt	Platinum	192, 194, 195, 196, 198
79	Au	Gold	197
80	Hg	Mercury	196, 198, 199, 200, 201, 202, 204
81	Tl	Thallium	203, 205
82	Pb	Lead	204, 206, 207, 208
83	Bi	Bismuth	209
84	Po	Polonium	[210] [211] [212] [214] [216] [218]
85	Ab	Alabamine	decaying isotopes only
86	Rn	Radon	[219] [220] [222]
87	Vi	Virginium	decaying isotopes only
88	Ra	Radium	[223] [224] [226]
89	Ac	Actinium	decaying isotopes only
90	Th	Thorium	[230] [232]
91	Pa	Protoactinium	[231]
92	U	Uranium	[234] [235] [238]
93	Np	Neptunium	decaying isotopes only
94	Pu	Plutonium	[238] [239]